CW00971116

NULLUS FUNIS SINE FIDULA

G
F
V

The Guild of
Funerary Violinists

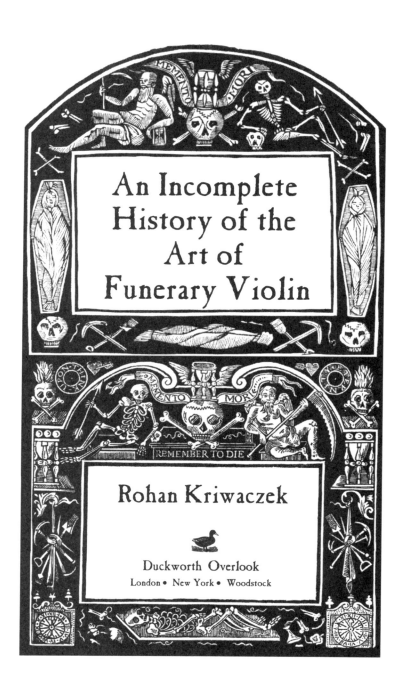

An Incomplete History of the Art of Funerary Violin

Rohan Kriwaczek

Duckworth Overlook
London • New York • Woodstock

First published in 2006 by
Duckworth Overlook

LONDON
Gerald Duckworth & Co. Ltd
90-93 Cowcross Street
London EC1M 6BF
inquiries@duckworth-publishers.co.uk
www.ducknet.co.uk

WOODSTOCK
The Overlook Press
One Overlook Drive
Woodstock, NY 12498
www.overlookpress.com
[for individual orders and bulk sales in the United States,
please contact our Woodstock office]

NEW YORK
The Overlook Press
141 Wooster Street
New York, NY 10012

A catalogue record for this book is available
from the British Library

ISBN 0 7156 3604 9 (UK)
EAN 9780715636046
ISBN 1-58567-826-0 (US)
EAN 9781585678266

Printed and bound in Great Britain by
CPD Ltd, Wales

Contents

Illustrations

Illustrations

Foreword

I have often been asked how I came to be involved with the Guild of Funerary Violinists, and, indeed, it is an interesting tale, to me at least. On completing my advanced diploma at the Royal Academy of Music with considerable honours in the early 1970s, my mind was filled with delusional dreams of becoming a concert soloist. Having done little other than play the violin since the age of seven, my unbounded naivety left me completely blind to the many eternal realities of the life of even the greatest of musicians, and for a number of years I floundered on the shoreline of popular success, endlessly surprised by the astonishing ignorance (as I saw it then) of the critics and audiences alike. But, alas, the fantastical determination and vigour of youth is soon worn out, and I was reluctantly forced to embrace the actuality of my existence.

Looking around me at the few colleagues and friends who had found a niche in the many-cornered industry of classical music, I saw that specialisation was the key to a successful career. Some colleagues were playing exclusively seventeenth-century music on period instruments, some only played modernist chamber music, one had moved from the violin to the musical saw, and one had a flourishing career in the more theatrical end of the industry, playing the works of J. S. Bach backwards (with some most musical results), though it must be admitted that after a brief television appearance his success was short-lived. What was needed, in the cynical seventies, was a gimmick, though I insisted on finding a gimmick with some degree of artistic integrity.

I had always been drawn to the more tragic and solemn works, indeed I believe that is what drew me to the violin in the first place – its inherent, deeply felt tragedy of tone – and so I resolved that henceforth I would only play the saddest of music; indeed, I would market my concerts as 'The Saddest Music in the World'. I vigorously delved into the libraries and archives of all of London's music colleges seeking ever sadder works, and by May 1975 I had assembled a fine repertoire of profoundly sonorous pieces and had embarked upon a tour of Northumberland. (I chose Northumberland both because of its distance from London – I was admittedly a little nervous of the critical response of the London scene – and because of the likelihood of a great storm blowing up during my concerts, a notion that I felt would add to the sense of gloom and tragedy I was there to impart.)

It was after one of these concerts that I was approached by a rather tall and stiff-looking gentleman, previously unknown to me, who invited me to attend a meeting of the Guild of Funerary Violinists. He was, it turned out, an amateur musician from London, who was in Northumberland to take the air because of a chronic case of nocardiosis (a debilitating lung disease caught by inhaling particles of earth), and a member of the board of the Guild, and though I have promised not to mention his name, or that of any members of the Guild since Herbert Stanley Littlejohn (who died in 1957), I will be forever grateful to him, as this introduction was to change the course of my life and vocation forever.

My initial impression of the Guild was not terribly inspiring; indeed, a more dreary collection of fellows could not be imagined, by me at least, although Dickens did at times come close. After a couple of meetings, where we discussed the Funerary Aesthetic, and the terrible events that befell the Guild, I was almost ready to leave for good, but then mention was made of the Guild's archives. Immediately my interest was rekindled, and I asked, nay begged, to be given access to whatever materials they might contain. It took a couple of months for me to gain the members' trust, but finally I was allowed to see the archives first hand.

Never in the history of record-keeping has there been a more chaotic, disorganised or neglected archive than this. The conditions were atrociously damp, pages were rotting, trunks were falling apart on top of each other, objects were stacked with all the coherence of a landslide, and I realised, at that moment, that it was my mission to preserve, collate and study whatever was not beyond saving. It was not long before the Guild's initial suspicion of my motives turned to enthusiasm, and even, at times, assistance, but the task itself was painstakingly slow. Much of the material amounted to little more than clues and fragments, and many years of earnest restoration and scholarship were necessary for even the simplest of stories to slowly reveal their full form.

In 1982, mainly as a result of my devoted research into their history, I was elected Acting Secretary of the Guild and, it must be admitted, used my position, in part, to nominate many new members and slowly eliminate the paranoid old guard, whose deep conservatism had only served to further condemn the Guild to isolation and ignominy. It was in this way that I was able to drag what had become little more than a stuffy gentleman's club for amateur musicians into the twenty-first century.

Although never a 'secret society', the persecution it had received during the nineteenth century, combined with indifference throughout the twentieth, had caused the Guild of Funerary Violinists to become a deeply secretive organisation over the years. When I first mentioned, in 1980, that some of these works should be available in the public domain, the reaction I received could be described as one of outright horror. It took until the year 2002 for the composition of the board to have changed substantially enough for provisional permission to be given for me to compile a book and an accompanying collection of CDs and sheet music, and even now there are many prohibitions: mainly, that I must mention very little of the Guild's history beyond 1841, and nothing whatever after 1914 – with a few notable exceptions that have been specifically agreed.

The history of the Art of Funerary Violin is deeply fragmentary, being made up of little more than glimpses, rumours, and occasional pieces of evidence that were missed by the agents of the Vatican during the Great Funerary Purges of the 1830s and 1840s. Since I embarked on this enterprise of discovery and consolidation many new documents have come to light: some as a result of my own efforts, some discovered independently, and some that had been in the vaults of museums and libraries all along, either incorrectly catalogued or simply never studied until now. Given this lack of sequential evidence, the story I am attempting to portray could be vastly altered at any time by some new discovery or conclusion. I am limited to reporting those few facts evidenced by materials I have seen for myself, representing the many rumours and insinuations that abound around the history of Funerary Violin, and making occasional speculations on my own part.

My intention in compiling this book is to bring the venerable Art of Funerary Violin once again out into the open space of public consciousness. It is a history defined by the evolution of art, politics and changing attitudes to mortality, which holds many lessons for us all. Like a great tree whose roots reach all the way back to the renaissance of modern man, it has born many fruits over the years: some that mouldered where they fell, some that sprouted shoots of their own, and some that were picked and carried many miles away to feed the souls of other musics in far distant lands. In the last thirty years a number of such works have come to light after years of idle obscurity, and may now be brought to the attention of scholars and musicians alike. That these pieces, born of man's courageous struggle with his most ancient of all enemies, should be heard once again in their true context, is undeniable by any who claim to value art and spirit above the tedium of everyday existence. I therefore offer up these pages, the humble fruits of many years of painstaking scholarship and research, that History may once again be rewritten, and perhaps, some day in the future, churchyards and cemeteries all across Europe may ring to the sonorously cathartic tones of the solo Funerary Violinist.

Rohan Kriwaczek B.A. (Hons) M.Mus F.G.F.V.
Acting President
The Guild of Funerary Violinists

Introduction

Being a General Introduction to the
Art and History of Funerary Violin

From its origins in the Elizabethan Protestant Reformation, to its final extinction amidst the guns of the First World War, the Art of Funerary Violin was characterised by many unique and frequently misunderstood qualities that set it quite apart from all other forms of music. Indeed, it is these distinctive characteristics that make it a truly unique genre, with its own specific concerns, aesthetic and function. Throughout the many changes in culture and society between the foundation of the Guild of Funerary Violinists in 1586 and the death of Niklaus Friedhaber (the last of the practising official Funerary Violinists) in 1915, it retained a trueness to its origins and function, and a commitment to purity of form and mode, unparalleled in any other western European musical tradition, which was due, in part, to the exclusive social role it played in relating the greatness of the higher classes directly to the ears of the lower classes.

This unique combination of pomp, ritual and spiritual expression was originally born out of the Protestant removal of the concept of intercession (that man, specifically a priest, can intercede with God on behalf of the soul of the deceased) from the funerary ritual, leaving a spiritual vacuum that was filled by the playing of the violin. How this shift happened so suddenly and so smoothly remains unknown, but at the time the violin had been in England for around forty years and was rapidly becoming noticed for its ability to be expressive both indoors and out, and George Babcotte (the founder of the Guild in 1586) was undoubtedly a man of considerable political intelligence and charisma. Much as was the case with the inevitable success of pop music in the 1950s, the cultural hole was there to be filled, and the time was right; and within two generations each town, and even village, had its own Funerary Violinist (usually part-time, and often doubling as a carpenter and coffin maker) and larger towns and parish councils would have a full-time official post with a modest annual salary (much of a Funerary Violinist's income was made through tips from the family and friends of the deceased).

By the end of the seventeenth century the practice had spread across much of Europe, particularly in the Protestant heartlands, but it had also taken root in France, Saxony, and many other more Catholic areas. Though at times reduced to village folk music, the tone was set at court: it was the great improvisers, and later composer-performers employed by the richest and most cultured in the land, who carved out the distinct musical language that was to give us not only the familiar funeral marches of today but many more subtle forms of spiritual and commemorative musics whose influence is cast over much of the more familiar classical repertoire of the nineteenth and twentieth centuries.

There are a number of much-quoted written accounts of performances by Funerary Violinists, dating right back to George Babcotte's performance at the funeral of Sir Philip Sidney in 1587, many of them profoundly moving and deeply tantalising, but until the end of the seventeenth century it was an entirely improvised tradition, and so has left no trace other than these tragically inadequate yet historically invaluable descriptions in words. The earliest known written example of Funerary Violin music is a short suite by Friedrich Heidebrecht dated 1670. Heidebrecht was a German-trained Funerary Violinist working for the court of Louis XIV, and it is thought that he was inspired to fix his compositions (rather than freely improvise) by his knowledge of the success, amongst lutenists at court, of the form of the *Tombeau,* a commemorative piece dedicated to a specific deceased person. These *Tombeaux* were a courtly adaptation of the music Funerary Violinists such as Heidebrecht had been playing, and he clearly saw the advantages to be gained by authorship at first hand.

What is puzzling is that these early composed representations of the form (by Heidebrecht, Addleston, Meunier, Faustmann, amongst others) bear such little resemblance to the accounts of improvised performances, often by the same artists. It can only be assumed that the transition to the written form proved a difficult process, and that success on paper, with its intention of spreading the work amongst many other players, depended upon a general gentrification of form, structure and melody. Though many of these late seventeenth- and eighteenth-century pieces are of considerable interest and occasionally display some of the more unusual modal and rhythmic characteristic associated with Funerary Violin, their courtly manners belie the true spirit of the tradition.

It is not until the emergence of Herr Hieronymous Gratchenfleiss in the 1770s that a composed form of the music finally emerges that embodies the full impact of the earliest written accounts. Though schooled in the contemporary harmony of his day by G. K. Bach in Hildesheim, Saxony, Gratchenfleiss soon abandoned it in favour of the bold rootedness of more modal writing. Almost all of his pieces are rooted on G, the lowest open string of the violin, which he often uses rhythmically like a bass drum. But not all his pieces take on the essence of a march. He crystallised the other more spiritual elements of the Funerary Violinist's function, evolving pieces to depict the panic of death, the seductive qualities of death, the dizzy confusion of death, and so forth: what survives of what must have been a prodigious output is more of an epic exploration of man's relationship with his own mortality than a set of functional ritual pieces. In his day his success as a sought-after Funerary Violinist brought him considerable fame, renown, and wealth, despite his many eccentricities, and his works were rapidly spread (though in very small quantities) around Europe, profoundly influencing the works of the next generation.

By the beginning of the nineteenth century Romanticism was well under way; artists had become prophets, death had become fashionable, and spiritual contemplation was no longer the province of religion alone. The 1810s in France saw the sudden appearance of popular funerary duels amongst Funerary Violinists (the soon to be deceased would leave a fragment of melody with his will, and two Funerary Violinists would improvise in turn upon the theme at the funeral, each attempting to draw more tragedy from it than his opponent – the winner being the artist who drew the most tears from the assembled crowd), and in England, Funerary Violinists such as Charles Sudbury were accepted as part of London's artistic establishment. The spiritual philosophy that underlay the Art had evolved into a semi-religious cult that briefly caught the imagination of all Europe. But, tragically, all this was soon to come to an end, as the Great Funerary Purges were about to sweep across Europe, eradicating almost every trace of this once flourishing art.

Scholars are, as yet, uncertain of the specific causes of the Great Funerary Purges, and many varied arguments have been posited and discredited over time. The theory given some currency today – that it was the result of a struggle between two factions within the Vatican for authority over grief and the spiritual exploitation thereof – will no doubt itself be refuted as more information becomes available. It is, of course, possible that the answer lies in the archives of the Vatican, and that one day these archives will reveal their secrets, but officially the Vatican has always denied all knowledge of the events.

What is known is that the Purges started spreading across Europe steadily in 1833, and originated in orders from Rome itself. The first signs went unnoticed: books went missing from libraries and private collections; there was a series of apparently unconnected burglaries in which paintings of Funerary Violinists were all that was taken; old violins with the traditional death's head scrolls were either vandalised or stolen (only to reappear years later 'restored' with a traditional scroll); and many pamphlets were circulated that condemned Funerary Violin as 'the music of the Devil'. But ultimately it amounted to the wholesale destruction of the Funerary Violin tradition, which had stretched back over 200 years, and the subsequent removal of any references to it.

It is doubtful whether such repression could have taken place, or such results been achieved, without the support and cooperation of government officials throughout Europe, but so little evidence remains that it is impossible to say. What little we do know has been painstakingly pieced together from a handful of fragments, and unsubstantiated and often unspoken rumours. Until a number of recent discoveries (such as the Hildesheim trunk, the writings of Charles Sudbury and the Chichester Suites), there was little solid evidence that such a rich tradition had existed at all.

* * * * *

There have always been two strains of Funerary Violin music. First, there is the ceremonial march, which was originally in 3 time to symbolise the broken stride of the deceased, and to distinguish it from religious music, which was in 4 time. Many of today's funeral marches are descended from the works of Funerary Violinists, and the form has remained largely unchanged over the years. Though many such marches were composed and performed for the nobility and the cultured, they were always aimed at the subjects, the tradesmen and the servants, as an affirmation of the social structure, and as such they were never allowed to become too abstract, or suffer the many indignities of overdone artistry. Second, there is the more cathartic spiritual element, usually performed as part of the oration or service. The actual function and duration of this element of the Funerary Violinist's role has varied considerably over the centuries, with the works performed ranging from the simplest of evocative hymns to monumental seven-movement suites designed to appease the spirit of the newly dead, drive off the devils, cleanse the soul, and send it on to the Lord. At times of Catholic suppression Funerary Violinists would slip in musical references to the banned liturgy to highlight the spiritual essence of their performance, but it was rare for this to be presented so specifically. What comes across most clearly in the surviving descriptions of their performances is the intense directness of their playing: how it seems to reach into the very hearts of those who are present.

To understand the true essence of the tradition, let us consider for a moment what a Funerary Violinist would have actually done, not from a practical but from an emotional perspective, for though manners and ideologies may have changed considerably over the years, emotions are unchanging, death remains death, and man's concern with it is unerring. The key to this is spiritual sensitivity. The chapel of rest, church or graveside is filled with strangers (to the violinist), all in a highly emotional and sometimes desperate state; the coffin containing their loved one is laid out at the front, and whilst everyone is still stirring, the violinist takes up his bow and begins the ritual. This moment is crucial, and if misjudged can lead to disaster.

In his tone the violinist must first convey the deep grief that is present in the gathering, and then transform it into a thing of beauty. By the time he is finished, a deep and plaintive calm should have descended, and the bereaved should be ready to hear the eulogy. To achieve this, the music must be simple. Any hint of flashiness, even the slightest breath of ego, will destroy the spell. This is music as magic, with the ability to transform the mood and perceptions of the audience in a way far beyond what is possible in the concert hall – and it only works on such a deep level because the audience is in a heightened emotional state. The violinist's is a position of great responsibility, akin in many ways to that of a priest or shaman, and should not be taken lightly.

It is for these reasons that the genre of Funerary Violin evolved in its own distinct manner, following a path of rooted modality and direct expression, and eschewing all displays of virtuosity, in terms of both performance and compositional artistry, in order to explore simply and honestly our relationship with our own and others' mortality, in all its many and varied historical and cultural aspects. Had it survived until today, who knows how it would have reflected our current disowning of death; however, it is certain that it would have proved more profound and deeply cathartic than the contemporary tendency towards recorded music played on a ghetto blaster. But then maybe a spiritless age deserves a spiritless death. It is not for me to judge.

1. This painting, originally entitled *The Funerary Violinist* by Petrus van der Velden (1813) was one of many casualties of the Great Funerary Purges of the 1830s. The Funerary Violinist, thought to have been Hendrik Van Baburan, who was leading the procession towards the churchyard on the left hand side of the picture, was cut off the painting some time after the picture disappeared in 1837. It reappeared in 1861 when it was purchased by the collector Richard Didcock. Now known as *The Dutch Funeral*, it hangs in Christchurch Art Gallery Te Puna o Waiwhetu, New Zealand.

A Brief Summary of Early Funeral Music

Ancient Flutes, Early Christians and the
First Great Purge of Funerary Music

The origins of the funeral procession are shrouded in the mists of time, though we can be certain that it goes back at least 10,000 years. Burial, being underground and hidden, provides considerable protection from environmental and cultural destruction, and as a result we know more about the burial, and therefore in some cases the funeral practices, of early human cultures than about anything else. Indeed, our knowledge of some early human cultures is based entirely upon the discovery of grave goods and the assumptions we can draw from them.

Contemporary accounts from ancient Egypt, Greece and Rome (amongst others) all indicate that musicians and dancers were an integral part of funeral processions, and that the instrument used was in each case the flute (the predominant melodic instrument of the period), in some cases accompanied by drums. Though no indication is given as to the actual nature of the music played, we know from Roman commentaries that the flute was an instrument profoundly associated with death, suggesting a lyrical, melodic approach to the musical expression of mortality. As early as 25,000 BC, burials around Europe (including those in Britain) were accompanied by walrus ivory bracelets and rods, perforated seashells and a sprinkling of red ochre, and given the obviously symbolic nature of these grave goods, it can be assumed that the placing of the body in or on the ground was accompanied by some degree of ritual, and very possibly a procession of some kind. The recent discovery, in 1995, in Slovenia (in the cave of Divje Babe) of a flute thought to be 45,000 years old and made of bone (from an extinct giant cave bear) suggests that it is at least possible that these early funerary rituals may also have involved the playing of a flute.

This association of the flute with death across a number of profoundly influential ancient cultures clearly indicates the choice of a melodically based music to express grief and mortality, in contrast to the more rhythmic music that we can assume was played on the harps, lyres and drums that we know to have been central to other aspects of each of these cultures. Indeed, it suggests that the association of grief with plaintive melodic lines is not just a modern historical association but one of those elemental vehicles of human expression that form the very basis of our musical languages. Just as times of social excitement, such as weddings or the moments before a battle, are universally accompanied by the beating of a drum, so the outpouring of grief is universally expressed through a magical exaggeration of the human voice; and for ancient cultures, the closest instrument to the voice was the flute. That the violin was to take over this role within a hundred years of its invention is both unsurprising and entirely natural, given its unique power and intensity and its ability to *sing* like no other instrument before it.

We know that it was the early Christians who put a stop to this ritual piping of the dead because of its pagan associations (the original Greek and Roman pan pipe was just such a flute, and not in fact the bundle of reeds today associated with the name), and its association with Pan, a god closely linked with the Devil in Christian minds, made it wholly anathema to any form of Christian spiritual music, as indeed musical instruments were to become in general (see the later chapter 'Paganini, the Vatican and Rumours of Demonic Association'). We will never know the mechanisms employed in this first great purge of funerary music in the third century AD, whether it came about through persuasion or repression, but the result was absolute throughout Christian Europe, and for the next thousand years the only music to be heard during funerary rites was the solemn intoning of the human voice. However, not all pagan musical practices were discarded, for the ringing of a bell (a suitably puritan and inexpressive instrument) was encouraged as death approached, to ward off the Devil and clear a path to God, in the hope of giving the spirit of the soon to be deceased a head start – a practice remarkably similar to the shaking of a rattle in ancient Egypt for the same purpose, and later taken up by Charles Sudbury in his Funerary Suites of the nineteenth century.

During this Catholic Christian period the musical emphasis swung from the depiction of grief to the stoical presentation of prayers for the dead. Masses would be sung for the dead, often repeatedly over months or even years if enough money was left to sponsor them, and the outward expression of emotion was of joy for the forthcoming resurrection, faith in the power of intercession (the saying of prayers to influence God's attitude toward the spirit of the deceased) and a general tone of solemnity without excessive sorrow. This stark and inexpressive religiosity was to dominate funeral rites throughout Europe until the Reformation, which, by sweeping away all funerary prayers and the very concept of intercession, left the door open to a more direct form of musical consolation. And with the arrival of the violin in England, in combination with the unique musical and political talents of George Babcotte, the Art of Funerary Violin was born.

The Subtle Art of the Funeral March

A History of Plagiarism and Forgetfulness

It is impossible to know when the first funeral marches were written specifically for that purpose. As already discussed, we can be fairly sure that funeral processions have been accompanied by music for as long as man has been civilised, but whether the music would have been conceived as a funeral march is entirely unknown. Funeral music itself was discouraged by the Catholic Church. As we have seen, the destruction of Catholicism by Henry VIII and the Reformation led to a new climate in which Funerary Violin was born, but there are no records of specific funeral marches until much later. This problem was compounded by the Great Funerary Purges of the 1830s and 1840s, during which many of the then existing records and scores were lost.

A thorough search of the monumental *Grove Dictionary of Music and Musicians*, the reference bible of the classical music tradition, reveals the full extent of the problem. Even the most obscure of Baroque or Renaissance musical forms is represented with substantial and comprehensive articles describing its intricate workings and listing many examples of the form; however, there are no references whatever to funeral marches, Funerary Violin or funeral music of any kind. This is particularly surprising since from Beethoven onwards the funeral march became a recognised and much referred to classical form, with fine examples by Beethoven, Chopin and Mahler standing amongst these composers' best known works (although the origins of such pieces, as shall be seen, are in many cases somewhat contentious).

Funerary Violinists were, by their very nature, solitary musicians and, traditionally, were kept separate from the circus of court and church musicians whose more plebeian role was to entertain the wealthy and inspire faith. Those who deal with death have always been stigmatised, and just as today it would seem bad taste to ask an undertaker to arrange a wedding (though they undoubtedly have the necessary contacts and organisational skills), it was always deemed to be bad luck for a Funerary Violinist to perform in any other more light-hearted context. This superstition resulted in Funerary Violinists being generally ostracised by other professional musicians of the day, seen as a separate culture unto themselves and, ultimately, becoming victims of the same historical snobbery that left folk music unacknowledged as of any social or artistic relevance until the early twentieth century. Indeed, the role of the Funerary Violinist lay uncomfortably between that of the court musician and the folk musician – performing to 'the people' in a vernacular idiom on behalf of the wealthy elite.

The forgetfulness of history is further exacerbated by the nature of the musical language, which for a long time remained an aural and semi-improvised tradition. This forgetfulness is clearly illustrated by our cultural memory of the Funeral of Queen Mary II in 1695. Costing well over £50,000 it was undoubtedly one of the most extravagant and expensive funerals ever staged, and was much celebrated in poetry, music and pictures for years after the event. The many engravings of the funeral procession clearly show Jonathan Heddleston, Master of the King's Funerary Violinists, set fourth back behind the hearse, and yet his musical contribution to the event has been entirely eclipsed by the music composed by the court musician Henry Purcell, which was performed at the culmination of the procession in Westminster Abbey.

That Purcell's *Funeral Music for Queen Mary* is still regularly played today whilst even the name of Jonathan Heddleston has been long forgotten is a clear demonstration of the many prejudices suffered by Funerary Violinists over the years, and yet another example of history being written by the victors; in this case the classical music tradition, which is today presented as if it were the only music being composed and performed before the birth of jazz in the early twentieth century. It is therefore no surprise that the funeral march itself has also been hijacked by the classical tradition, and today it is Beethoven, Chopin, Grieg and Mahler who are credited with the most masterful demonstrations of the form whilst the true composers of the works they shamelessly plagiarised have by now been long forgotten.

The funeral march itself is a most particular musical form with its own specific intentions and methods of realisation. Over the centuries many other kinds of music have been mistaken for funeral marches, and it has often been assumed that any solemn work in slow 4/4 time can be considered a funeral march; but the distinct essence of the true form can be immediately recognised by any worthy scholars of Funerary Violin and its offshoots. An early example of this confusion, from the classical music tradition, would be the march that opens and closes the aforementioned *Funeral Music for Queen Mary* by Henry Purcell. The context of this piece (correctly entitled 'March', not 'Funeral March'), in a set of funerary pieces, has led many to infer that it is itself a funeral march. Of course the notion is ridiculous, as the piece contains few of the requisite elements that would elevate it to such a status, but the misinterpretation is understandable given the general level of ignorance about such matters amongst musicians and the general public today. This march is clearly a slow heraldic march, solemnised into the context of the queen's funeral, but still calculated to underline the military and hierarchical status of the queen, her family and her successors.

Admittedly these elements have been known to creep into the practice of Funerary Violinists and their funeral marches, but at their best these are always tempered by other elements depicting transformation, the cleansing of the soul, and a spiritual evolution that is entirely absent from Purcell's 'March'. In addition, the latter work was probably intended, at least in part, as a solemn caricature of the playing of Jonathan Heddleston, which Purcell would have known well. Indeed there was, since 1688, a famous rivalry between the two of them as a result of King William's choice of Heddleston to be the sole performer at the memorial service for King James II. This rivalry escalated over the following years into something of a scandal when, in 1694, libellous accusations were levelled against Heddleston by a number of the king's musicians, under the leadership of Purcell himself, which resulted in a trial before the Privy Council for 'lewd behaviour unbefitting a servant of the King'. Ultimately Heddleston was found innocent, but the commissioning of a great funerary work from Purcell upon the death of Queen Mary was undoubtedly intended to put Heddleston in his place, as not only was he not invited to play at the culmination of the ritual, as was traditional, but he was also barred from entering the Abbey altogether. (He did, however, get his small revenge when, later that same year, he performed at the funeral of Purcell himself, despite rumours that he had been involved in the composer's death by arranging for him to be poisoned. Nothing was ever proven, and the death was finally officially put down to 'exposure'. Heddleston's performance at the funeral was said to be amongst his worst, and least appropriate.)

The difference between a solemn march and a funeral march is both subtle and profound. A solemn march can be militaristic or heraldic in its intention; it can express the empty despair of a battle lost, or the heady solemnity of a victory well won; and it can even, in certain examples, express the stoical acceptance of death. But a solemn march is always tied to a single and simple purpose, and through rigour and restraint will express nothing but that single purpose. A true funeral march is an infinitely more complex and subtle form, always standing in two worlds at once: expressing both the outward formality of a well crafted ritual and the inner despair of a desperate grief; portraying both the tragedy of a spirit lost forever to this world and the triumphant ascension of a soul unto the eternity of the hereafter; both inward- and outward-looking, containing and expressing the profound emotions of an entire life now defined, and yet lost to us forever. The finest examples, such as the works of Herr Gratchenfleiss, Charles Sudbury and Pierre Dubuisson, tread this subtle line with elegance and modesty: at times moving effortless between major and minor; at times rising up as if to burst with uncontained emotion, only to be constrained at the outer limits by the inevitable imposition of ritual and form; at times delving to the very depths whilst always maintaining an intensity and focus so proud that the voice of humanity itself seems to be speaking with the dead, leaving them both scorned and consoled, derided and reprised; cutting through the dogma of their long-forgotten lives with all the skill of a surgeon and all the passion of a priest.

The earliest known funeral march to bear that title formally was composed by Kaspar Ignaz Faustmann in 1722, although its authenticity is questionable (see the chapter on Herbert Stanley Littlejohn). It was the funeral marches of Herr Gratchenfleiss, forty years later, that brought the form to its apotheosis and laid the foundations for the later great works of Sudbury and Dubuisson. Gratchenfleiss defined much of the aesthetic and many of the techniques that are still familiar at funerals today: the bold use of repetition; the striking of the G string as if it were a bass drum; the notion that the dronal aspect of modality created a necessary focus that would be disturbed by the intrusion of too functional a harmonic language. His funeral marches were bold and intense, carrying a great weight of responsibility on their shoulders, yet still managing to express that subtle duality so essential to the form, and the undeniable strength and commitment of these compositions inspired something of a popular following. As a result, what had for a long time been perceived as a purely functional ritual music, albeit profoundly expressive, was suddenly a recognised popular form, and for the first time you might have heard an artisan or tradesman whistling one of Gratchenfliess's funeral marches to himself as if it were an ordinary tune. Indeed, to this very day the funeral march subtitled 'The Noble March of Death' remains a distinctive part of the repertoire of the Gorandovic family gypsy brass band, and though recognised by them as a funeral march, they tell me they have also played it at weddings and world music festivals, where, in another example of shifting authorship, it is considered a traditional gypsy march.

By the 1790s, in the wake of the French Revolution, a number of funeral marches had become deeply embedded in the popular psyche, appearing in street entertainments and music hall shows as grotesque caricatures of their former selves, in much the same way that today you might hear a version of the funeral march popularly attributed to Chopin in a computer game soundtrack, or even as a mobile phone ringtone. Amongst these works was a *Trauermarsch* by the Munich-based Funerary Violinist Ulmer Diederich – dated 1787 – which was to become the first of many such works to be hijacked by the closed world of classical music, and by no less a composer than Ludwig van Beethoven.

There is no doubt that Beethoven would have heard Diederich's *Trauermarsch,* as it was being played all over the Austro-Hungarian Empire throughout the late 1790s, and I would suggest that his theft of the first part of the work for use in his third symphony was not intended as plagiarism, but as a self-conscious

reference to a popular funeral march with the intention of adding further levels of symbolism to his music. A brief examination of the two melodies reveals the striking similarities.

To blame Beethoven himself for the wholesale theft of the Funerary Violin repertoire by classical composers who followed is perhaps a little unfair, although many scholars have indeed gone that far, and a close examination of their arguments reveals them to be entirely sound. Beethoven could be pardoned: he had, after all, only quoted the head-tune of Diederich's masterful work. Frédéric Chopin was to take the whole of Joseph Sea-Boone's Funeral March in A minor and reproduce it, with very few alterations, in his Piano Sonata no. 2, even including the rocking motion between the fifth and minor sixth in the accompaniment – ultimately stealing the credit for what has become the most famous and popular funeral march of all time.

Very little is known about Sea-Boone. He is registered in the Stockport parish records as the official parish Funerary Violinist between 1807 and 1829. It is thought that he then embarked on a tour of Europe, as a small collection of his funerary works for solo violin were published by Diabelli & Co. (Vienna) in 1831, and it is indeed possible that Chopin himself might have heard Sea-Boone performing in Vienna in November of 1830. However Chopin came to the work, it is likely that he would have viewed it as a form of folk music and therefore ripe for the picking, such was the inherent conceit of artists of the period. That Diabelli published Sea-Boone's works at all is testament to the Romantic taste for 'folklore' and 'quaint old ways' that was sweeping through Europe's artistic circles. Of course, in both of the above cases the composers in question placed the funeral marches into larger-scale contexts to disguise the theft, and counterbalanced them with uplifting melodies in a gratuitous attempt to present them as classical concert hall music, but the spirit and intention of the music is clearly born of the Funerary Violin tradition, and this wanton burglarising of the Funerary repertoire in the early nineteenth century was just one of many signs of the impending destruction and dismantling of the once great tradition that was Funerary Violin.

As is often the case in art, the most powerful and enigmatic works, the funeral marches of Sudbury and Dubuisson, were created just as the culture from which they grew was facing its boldest and final threat. The Great Funerary Purges of the 1830s and 1840s were to spell the wholesale destruction of this venerable practice and drive the few remaining artists underground, but not before a last grand flourish of creativity had fixed the form of the seven-movement Funerary Suite and, within that suite, had defined the morbidly ambiguous and secretly symbolic funeral march once and for all.

It is society's eternal tragedy that those who aspire to greatness and reach their goal must necessarily be brought down by those they stand above. How many times have the grandest achievements of man been destroyed by a jealous and aggressive multitude? How many temples have been torn to the ground by hordes of unbelieving soldiers in search of plunder? How many visionaries were cast into the blackness of obscurity in the interest of politics and power? How many libraries were burned? How much has been lost, and lost again? It is the very nature of man to build too high and be destroyed! It is the very nature of man to see a thing of beauty and leave it broken and dead, that none thereafter might possess that which seems unobtainable. So it was with Sudbury and Dubuisson: both murdered by the agents of the Catholic Church for the threat that they allegedly posed to God himself; both suffering the post-mortem indignity of attempted erasure from history. That the small handful of works that we do have survived at all is a vindication of their eternal nature, and that strain of luck, which, in retrospect, seems somehow to be preordained.

The major achievement of Sudbury and Dubuisson was their ultimate definition of the sacred duality in the funeral march, and the consequent evolution and fixing of the seven-movement Funerary Suite. Regardless of the sometimes questionable spiritual philosophy that lay behind their works (discussed in greater detail in the chapter on Charles Sudbury), the ambiguous musical expression of these ideas encapsulated both a complex mystical message and a pure invocation of the spirit of the first half of the nineteenth century. Had the tide of religious and political intolerance not turned against them, who knows where this visionary path might have led. And yet, of course, history always acts for a reason, and it may be that the essentially sincere intentions of the venerable tradition of Funerary Violin were doomed to fade into obscurity, amidst the decadence and self-indulgence that Romanticism soon descended into. It is indeed hard to see what role a musician of Sudbury's spiritually pure (through perhaps deluded) vision could play when competing against Mahler's monstrously overdone symphonic follies, which ooze with contrived tragedy and intemperate sentimentality.

By the time of their deaths (in 1841 and 1838 respectively), Sudbury and Dubuisson had set an unattainable standard in the construction and execution of the funeral march: one that has been mimicked and caricatured ever since in shallow-minded two-dimensional efforts by the classical tradition. Had their works not been so savagely suppressed, and had they thus remained in their rightful place at the centre of our culture, there is no doubt that the later nineteenth-century composers would never have got away with such a charade in place of creativity. But fate did intercede, and it is only now, with the discovery of these, the most exalted examples of the Funerary Art, that we can finally reassess the nineteenth-century perception and execution of the funeral march with any degree of perspective and genuine objectivity.

2. John Dunn the Younger, photographed here in 1852, was one of a number of Funerary Violinists who were to betray the sacred nature of their tradition after the Great Funerary Purges. Unable to continue in the profession in the hostile climate of the 1850s, he wrote popular and often bawdy lyrics to the melodies he had previously played in sincere contemplation of mortality, and performed them in a comedy duo with Dorothy Thrimble in music halls all over London. Their act, in which he took the role of a comedy Funerary Violinist before bursting into song, and she played a corpse re-animated through the power of his music and unrequited love, was a considerable success throughout the 1860s, and made 'Thrimble and Dunn' something of a household name. Dunn died on stage at the Golders Green Hippodrome in 1871, at the age of sixty-two, whilst performing this role, in what some have called an act of divine intervention.

The Erroneous Dirge of
George Babcotte

AS IT VVERE PLAYED BEFORE
HER MAJESTIE THE QVEENE

At the most vvorthy fvneral of

Sir Philip Sidney
on
17th October 1586

Recreated from a vvritten accounte of confiderable detail by
Thomas Dinfley in the yeare of Our Lord 1697

LONDON ;
Printed by R.K. for *The Gvild of Funerary Violinifts,*
and are to be fold at the fhop in the Inner-Temple,
neere the Chvrch, 1697.

3. The cover of the *Erroneous Dirge* of George Babcotte, rescued from the fire at the offices of the Guild of Funerary Violinists in 1841 by the then secretary, Matthew Connisten. Despite the claim in the title that it is the actual music performed by Babcotte at the funeral of Sir Philip Sidney, the subtitle reveals that it was, in fact, composed by Thomas Dinsley in 1697, as a recreation strongly based on a detailed written account of Babcotte's performance by the poet Tom Watson.

6. This picture dated 1589, the oldest artefact in the archive of the Guild of Funerary Violinists, was traditionally thought to be a portrait of George Babcotte. Painted on a pine panel, and measuring only 12 cm x 8 cm, it took pride of place above the grand conference table at the Guild's various headquarters for over 400 years. It was not until 1996 that this attribution was called into question when restoration work revealed the name 'Christopherus Strome' faintly inscribed on the back, together with an artist's mark, 'J.C', thought to have been that of the Southwark artist Jonah Cobbe. Whether 'Christopherus Strome' is the name of the sitter cannot be proven, and some members of the Guild insist that it is in fact the name of the patron who commissioned the work. However, in the opinion of the author there is no evidence, other than the picture's provenance, to link the image to George Babcotte. Who 'Christopherus Strome' was is entirely unknown.

George Babcotte

The First of the Funerary Violinists

Born in Canterbury in 1542, George Babcotte lived and worked in a period rich in ferment and characterised by much chaotic change; a period destined to evolve numerous new approaches to art, science and ritual, with many great thinkers and doers pushing at all the known boundaries of man's understanding. The newly established English Protestant philosophy was hacking away at the old superstitions, both sacred and secular, with varying degrees of success, and new instruments of art and science were crossing the Channel for the first time, revolutionising many aspects of contemporary thought. Babcotte's career is inextricably tied up with the many political twists and turns of this period and driven, as will be seen, by his own ability to seize events and bend them to his advantage.

Joseph Babcotte was head jailer, and later sheriff, to Sir Edward Kerne. In 1542, shortly after the birth of his first son, George, he was sent, with his master, to apprehend a number of individuals suspected of being secretly practising Jews. Amongst these were a group of six musicians from Italy (Alexander, Ambrose and Romano of Milan, Albert and Vincenzo of Venice and Juan Maria of Cremona). They had been brought to England by Thomas Cromwell in 1540 on the orders of Henry VIII, who had wanted to improve the standards of music in his court for his impending marriage to Anne of Cleves, and they are listed as being 'performers on the viol and violin', making them the first violinists in England. Privy Council records dated 4 February 1542 record their apprehension by Phillip Hobbin, Sir Edward Kerne and Dr Peter, and an inventory of the goods of the individuals involved; this included six viols (of various sizes), two violins, two violas and a violoncello. It is worth noting that this uneven number of instruments – six viols yet only five members of the violin family – was not questioned at the time, but clearly suggests that an instrument may have gone missing. (After their captivity, during which two of them died, the allegedly Jewish musicians were allowed to leave England quietly. Some months later Ambrose returned with a replenished troop and once again took up his court position, holding it for the following fifty-three years until his death in 1594. His sons were to perform at the funeral of Queen Elizabeth I under the direction of George Babcotte.)

There are no further records of George Babcotte, beyond his baptism on 16 February 1542 (in the old English calendar, making it 26 February in our current Gregorian calendar) in St Mary's Church, until 1566, when he is listed as 'performyng on the vyolyn' in George Gascoigne's play *Supposes* (a translation of Ariosto's *I Suppositi* of 1509) at a 'carnival' at Gray's Inn. Until recently there had been much debate amongst scholars as to where he had acquired such an instrument, as there were still very few violins in England, each accounted for and belonging to the musicians of Queen Mary's court, and such an instrument would cost a princely sum (around the yearly salary of four serving maids and a cook). However, recent study of the Privy Council records suggests very strongly that this may have been the same instrument that was missing from the 1542 inventory.

We have no way of knowing how Babcotte learnt to play, nor what he played, but a letter from John Lyly to Edward De Vere, that was preserved in the archives of Oxford University, gives a clear indication of the impression he made:

Gascoigne's Supposes is a veritable triumph. A truer translation could not be conceived of, and the play was both sumptuous and gay. The finest performance was undoubtedly that of John Stanley as Pasyphilo, the parasite, though Peter Nashe made a fine wench in the role of the old hag, Psyteria. Throughout, the whole was musically accompanied by a George Babcotte, a musician whom I have not come upon before, on an instrument called the violin. This is not unlike the vielle though infinitely more focussed and penetrating. His playing was truly the saddest sound I have ever heard, and though at times inappropriately, it moved the whole of the crowd to tears repeatedly. This is a man worth watching, as I am sure he may prove useful. After the carnival I approached the said George Babcotte and we talked over a bowl of broth and more than a pitcher of sugared sack. He is certainly a gruff gentleman, but is capable of more than a little charm. He claims to have attended the Canterbury King's School for four years before his family moved to London, though I suspect this may be less than true, as my attempts to address him in both Latin and Greek fell upon deaf ears … [translated from the original French]

It is not known how Babcotte came to be working in the theatre, but this single letter tells us more about his early years than any other document. It is clear that he attended (or claimed to have attended) the King's School at Canterbury, that his family had moved to London when he was in his early teens, and that he was poorly educated, in comparison to his theatrical peers. It also finally dispels any doubts as to his ownership of a violin (some scholars had suggested that the term vyolyn on the playbill was a misspelling or misrepresentation of vielle). It demonstrates that he had a tendency towards tragedy in his playing, even when it was not deemed to be entirely appropriate. As we shall see, the impression he made upon Lyly was greatly propitious, and he was to work for both Lyly and De Vere on many occasions in the future; indeed, he was to perform at both of their funerals.

In addition, it is worth mentioning the striking effect that the violin itself had on Lyly's ears. It was clearly a much more powerful and penetrating sound than Lyly had come to expect from a stringed instrument, and it is this impressive new sound, together with his obviously soulful playing, that marked Babcotte apart as a musician. At this time the only place where violins could be heard in England was in the court orchestra, and there was still a clear distinction between indoor and outdoor music. To our current knowledge, Babcotte was the first musician in England to demonstrate the potential success of the violin as both an indoor and an outdoor instrument, and in presenting it publicly, rather than in the private confines of the court, he quickly found a following.

Six years later, in 1572, Babcotte's name appeared on the billing of another play by Gascoigne: *Jocasta – a tragedy*, written as a wedding masque for Lord Montague. In 1576 it seems that he joined The Children of the Chapel Royal, a children's theatre group that was based in the old monastery of the Black Friars, between St Paul's and the Thames. (Interestingly, the building, after disestablishment, had been divided into a private theatre and a fencing school.) This company was soon joined by Paul's Boys and The Children of the Earl of Oxford, and it is generally conceded that by 1582 the three companies were united under the patronage of Edward De Vere, the Earl of Oxford. Between 1576 and 1580 Babcotte's name appears frequently in association with performances at the Blackfriars, and between 1580 and 1582 he toured extensively with Oxford's Men, including performances in Bristol, Cambridge, Dover, Hythe, Norwich and Coventry

(1580), Norwich, Ipswich and Coventry (1581), and Bristol and Ticknall (1582). However, after 1582 his name is no longer seen in association with any theatrical troops, more than likely as the result of an unfortunate injury incurred during an affray (one of many throughout the year of 1582–3) between Oxford's Men, and the men of Thomas Knyvet.

These 'brabbles and Frays', as Burghley called them, were caused, it is thought, by a private issue of honour – Knyvet was the uncle of Anne Vavasour, mother of De Vere's illegitimate son. Whatever the specific issue between them, the feud seems to have escalated by 1582, resulting in the first of a number of public fights between the employees of the two men, in and around Blackfriars. The first of these affrays was on 18 June 1582, and was well documented at the time, but it was the second such fight, on 22 June outside the Blackfriars theatre, that involved Babcotte. There were two eye-witnesses whose testimony is recorded: Daniel Bothame, Surgeon, and William Crouche, Mercer, both of Fleet Street. Their stories are the same, though some details are given by one and omitted by the other. I offer here a combined account:

> *Upon Friday last, in the afternoon, [they] saw one called Gastrell and named to be my Lord of Oxford's man draw his sword upon 3 or 4 of Mr Knyvet's men. And one of Mr Knyvet's men said twice or thrice: 'Put up thy sword Gastrell, we will not deal with thee here, there is no place here,' and xxxred [illegible] the street to bear witness. Gastrell replied and said he would fight with them, and one Babcotte, of Oxford's Men, would have parted the fray and willed Gastrell to put up his sword, which he did accordingly. And then one of Mr Knyvet's men said: 'Gastrell, another time use thy discretion.' Whereupon Gastrell drew again and ran upon one of Mr. Knyvet's men furiously; and they struck 5 or 6 blows, and Mr Knyvet's man hurt Gastrell. The rest of Mr Knyvet's men had their swords drawn but struck not at all. Babcotte, of Oxford's Men, with his sword drawn, would have parted the fray and (according to Bothame) was hurt by chance, by Gastrell, losing the larger part of his nose.*

Such an injury, although by no means mortal, would have been most unfortunate at the time as facial mutilations were still practised in the punishment of criminals, and hence Babcotte now wore the mark of a thief – a situation that would have made it impossible for him to find honest work, were it not for his courtly and literary connections. Whether it was because his injury came from one of De Vere's own men, or because of a genuine respect for his artistry, De Vere was very generous in his compensation to Babcotte, not only providing him with a written declaration of the 'true and honeste loyalty' that led to this disfigurement, but also an annual pension of £10. (De Vere was renowned for his patronage of the arts, and his overdone generosity was to lead him near to bankruptcy. In 1586, to rescue him from penury, the queen granted the Earl an annual pension of £1,000.) In addition, De Vere's accounts for 1582 include the commissioning of a 'fyne modele nose, of walrus ivorie, and paynted to be moste real' from 'Thomas Woode of Brooke Street, two shillings six pence'.

It was as a result of this injury that Babcotte's career changed direction, no doubt driven in part by the freedom this pension now provided him, and the notoriety he had acquired as De Vere's 'noseless fiddler'. But to fully understand how he was to become the first of the Funerary Violinists, we must go back twenty-four years to 1558.

The accession of Queen Elizabeth I to the English throne in 1558 brought with it a savage reassertion of Protestant doctrine, affecting all elements of life's rituals, not least of them the death rites. Under Elizabeth's rule superstition was to be stripped away, and particularly the notion of intercession after death. The much-corrupted Catholic Church had long been taking money for prayers after death to be said to intercede with God on the soul's behalf, and greater profits were made from selling whole masses on behalf of the souls of the wealthy. Under Elizabeth this was immediately banned, and indeed any conscious consideration of the afterlife was discouraged (the Doctrine of Purgatory had itself been abolished with the Reformation). The 1552 Order for Burial had drastically shortened the funeral service and removed any notion of praying for the dead, and this had itself been revised in 1559's *Book of Common Prayer*. Over the next few decades the role of the Church in burials was stripped away still further, ultimately leading to *A Directory for the Publique Worship of God,* established by Parliament in 1644. This directory stated that no minister need be present at a burial: if one happened to be there his role was to put those attending 'in remembrance of their duty', which included having the body 'immediately interred, without any ceremony'.

With this drastic reduction in the religious element at the burial service, the socially regenerative aspects of the funeral ritual took on a far greater (and more expensive) role. Persons of note or status would have a heraldic funeral – as the name suggests, this meant a funeral governed and orchestrated by the Heralds of the College of Arms (forerunners of the undertaking profession, wearing tabards with the arms of the queen herself). These heralds were concerned more with the secular transfer of roles and honours than the interment of the body. The higher up the hierarchy, the more death threatens the stability of society itself, and the greater the reinforcement had to be. This soon led to the establishment of a strict code for the conduct of the funeral procession (a baron would have seven principal mourners whereas an earl would have nine, a duke eleven, and so forth).

In 1584 the records for the Heralds of the College of Arms dictated the addition of a Funerary Violinist to the procession of all of the status of baron and above. A reigning monarch was to have four Funerary Violinists, and heirs to the throne must have two. This is the very first mention of Funerary Violinists in any record found to date, and in all accounts so far discovered of heraldic funerals between 1584 and 1590, the name of the musician employed was George Babcotte. How he came to take on this role is unknown, but many scholars have suggested that it was Thomas Knyvet, Gentleman of the Privy Chamber, who had instigated this addition to the code of practice, in gratitude for Babcotte's intervention in the Blackfriars affray, without which he might well have lost another of his men (as Gastrell was a notoriously fine swordsman).

It must be remembered that Babcotte was not from a family of musicians, and his sudden rise in status did not go unnoticed by the London Guild of Musicians. In 1585 the London Guild added a rule stating that violins must play in groups of three or more, a move almost certainly intended to undermine Babcotte by either preventing him from fulfilling this unique new role, or forcing his resignation from the Guild. Babcotte responded, with typical gusto, by founding the Guild of Funerary Violinists, which, thanks to his by now numerous contacts at court, was officially recognised on 6 June 1586 (old English calendar).

There are a number of records of Babcotte's performing at heraldic funerals during the late 1580s and early 1590s, most notably that of Sir Philip Sidney on 16 February 1587 (he had died at Arnheim on 17 October 1586 from a bullet wound to the thigh received at the battle of Zutphen). Whether Babcotte had known Sir Philip Sidney personally is not reported, but given his courtly and literary connections at the time it is not improbable that they had met.

The funeral itself was a tribute to heraldic excess. At the head of the procession were thirty-two official mourners, one for each year of the deceased's life, followed by officers on foot and horse regiments. After them came Sidney's standard (a cross of St George with additional porcupines), sixty gentlemen and yeomen, followed by his chief physician, surgeon and steward. Next came squires and

5. This popular late eighteenth-century engraving entitled *The Death of Sir Philip Sidney* (1796) clearly demonstrates the mythological status Sir Philip Sidney soon acquired after his death. Sent to Flanders by Queen Elizabeth I to assist the people of the Netherlands in their fight against Spain, he was shot in the leg and died twenty-two days later of an infected wound. The story goes that when offered water by his surgeons he turned to a dying soldier, saying, 'Thy need is greater than mine own,' thus earning himself a place in the book of popular martyrs. It was Babcotte's association with Sir Philip Sidney's funeral that established both him and the Art of Funerary Violin in general as essential to a good and noble burial. Thus the moment depicted here could be said to be one of the most important single occasions in the foundation of Funerary Violin, not only as an independent genre but also as a central pillar of funerary practice throughout Britain and Europe for the following 250 years.

knights of his kinsfolk (including Sir Francis Drake), followed by the preacher of the sermon (in a non-religious role) and two chaplains. Then came the pennon bearer, followed by two of Sidney's horses – one trailing a broken lance, the other carrying a reversed battle axe. These were followed by the standard bearer, leading the five heralds carrying the 'hatchments and dignity' of Sidney's knighthood (his spurs, gauntlets, helmet, shield and standard). These were followed by Babcotte, playing his 'mournful dirges' and leading the coffin with its velvet pall (carried by Fulke Greville, Edward Dyer, Edward Wotten and Thomas Dudley), behind which followed the chief mourner, Philip's younger brother, Robert Sidney, and other kinsfolk. Finally, following these, were the gentlemen ushers and noblemen on horseback, representatives of the States of Holland, the Lord Mayor of London, officials of the City, members of the Company of Grocers, and 300 citizens of London, each with their weapons reversed, marching three abreast. This scene gives a clear impression of the heraldic funeral at its most grandiose, and it is easy to see how secular ritual and social reinforcement had replaced any direct notion of religious intercession. Sir Robert Sidney's position as first behind the coffin was a direct presentation of the continuity of lineage.

On the Death of Sir Philip Sidney

GIVE pardon, bleſſeèd ſoul, to my bold cries,
If they, importune, interrupt thy ſong,
Which now with ioyfull notes thou ſing'ſt among
The angel-quiriſters of th' heauenly ſkies.
Giue pardon eke, ſweet ſoul, to my ſlow eyes,
That ſince I ſaw thee now it is ſo long,
And yet the tears that vnto thee belong
To thee as yet they did not ſacrifice.
I did not know that thou wert dead before;
I did not feel the grief I did ſuſtain;
The greater ſtroke aſtoniſheth the more;
Aſtoniſhment takes from vs ſenſe of pain;
I ſtood amazed when others' tears begun,
And Babcotte's dirges wrung our hearts as one.

Henry Conſtable 1587

27

For the funeral itself, St Paul's Cathedral was hung in black. After a lengthy sermon (the subject of which has been lost), Babcotte performed for a full five minutes on the violin, immediately followed by a double volley from soldiers positioned outside in the churchyard. How the timing of this was negotiated will never be known, but it made a great impression on those assembled.

There are two documents, both now well known, that give us an impression of Babcotte's role in the service. The first is a poem by Henry Constable, commemorating the funeral and Sir Philip Sidney himself (this was just one of many elegiac verses penned in honour of the event).

Far more interesting, however, is a letter written by Tom Watson, a musically literate poet, to Henry Percy, Earl of Northumberland. In it he describes the funeral service, and gives considerable detail of both Babcotte's demeanour and the precise structure of the music he played:

> *The sermon ended with a long pause for contemplation, and it was as we sat, with our eyes closed, musing upon the tragedy of events that had unfolded, now many months earlier, and the great loss that this had brought us, that Babcotte silently arose from his chair, and with the subtlety of an angel, put bow to string. He certainly cut an extraordinary figure, dressed all in white, with the customary black ribbons tied around the scroll of his violin, and around his (some would say inappropriately large) silver embroidered codpiece, but it was his playing that impressed us all so deeply. With a look of tremendous earnestness and strain upon his tragically disfigured face, he drove from the violin a kind of music so deeply sad and yet impassioned, the like of which I am sure has not been heard before in all of Christendom. From the very first notes we were caught in his wondrous spell, and at the end we were left aghast for some moments, before the sudden volleys of musket fire stole the magic from us, and made us realise, once again, where we were.*

> *I am but a humble student of music, and bow to the greater knowledge of my many colleagues and friends who know the workings of that particular muse far more intimately than myself, but knowing that you have yourself gained some expertise in such matters, and take a considerable interest in this most enigmatic of arts, I have made an earnest attempt at describing the workings, as I could deduce them in the moment, of this most tragically spirited performance.*

I believe his violin to have been tuned to perfect 5ths though I cannot be sure of the root note.

He opened with a sombre declaration of a four note ground bass, played so slowly that each note seemed to hold eternity. This ground rose from the root note to the minor 6th, then down to the 4th, and finally up to the 5th. This single pattern seemed ever-present underneath his playing – no matter how impassioned he became, it was never lost. As the music slowly unwound he would add, first tentatively, and then with more confidence, subtle ornamentation that slowly evolved ever further into great cascades of notes, forever increasing in pitch and intensity. Just as we thought the music had reached its peak he changed the rhythm to shorten the bars, adding considerable intensity in one simple yet remarkable step, and then again a few moments later. Finally it seemed we would be returned to ourselves, as the music slowly descended from the ether, when the ground stepped in once again, plain and bold, and a new series of elaborations began to unfold. This time the music seemed more determined, and reached a peak with what felt like less effort and yet seemed somehow richer and deeper. His time changes seemed less pronounced in this second time round, and though it was the shorter half, it gave the impression of being still more monumental than the first. Finally, after what must have been at least five minutes, his music slowly wound itself down, ending in what seemed like both a protest against, and a resignation to, the will of Death. We felt that we had been taken to heaven, and were now laid, gently, back upon the grass of England's fair hills. It was a music I will never forget, and I earnestly pray that Babcotte survives me long enough to play at my own funeral, as never before has a man been so graced in the absence of his soul ... [translated from the original Italian]

This single document is the only record we have of what Babcotte actually played and there is no indication that his music was ever written down. Whether he was improvising or had planned every note cannot be ascertained from what little evidence we have, as both practices were common at the time. However, as we shall see, this letter did result in an interesting series of recreations over a hundred years later. (It is worth noting that Tom Watson did get his wish, as Babcotte was to play at his funeral in 1592.)

There is some evidence to suggest that, as the result of this noteworthy performance, Babcotte himself became a regular at Court, and certainly by 1590 he seems to have found favour with the Queen. The London Guild of Musicians, and specifically Ambrose Lupo (the same Ambrose who had come to Henry's Court in 1540, and whom Babcotte's father had arrested, and from whom it is thought Babcotte's violin was stolen), was increasing its pressure to prevent Babcotte from performing solo. They petitioned the Privy Council to ban the Guild of Funerary Violinists on the grounds that it only had one member and therefore couldn't truly be a Guild, or any other official organisation. Babcotte, in turn, petitioned the Queen herself, requesting permission for two remarkable amendments to his Guild's prospectus, both of which were granted on 20 September 1590 (old English calendar). First, he requested permission to make his Guild a National Guild, the first in Europe, on the grounds that for Funerary Violin to retain its true spiritual power it must be performed solo, and that therefore there was only room for one such performer in each town. Second, he requested permission to allow honorary members, who were not expected to perform on the violin but showed sympathy or enthusiasm for the form. In addition, the Guild was granted a royal warrant.

Although the majority of the Guild's early records were destroyed in the Great Fire of 1666, and many of those that survived were in turn seized or destroyed by the Catholic Church in the Great Funerary Purges of the 1830s and 1840s, there is a tantalising list of Guild members dated 1593, which survived as a result of being lost until 1978, when it was discovered, together with a wooden panel portrait of Babcotte himself, during minor refurbishments of the offices of Canterbury Cathedral. In this list there are only two full members, these being Babcotte himself, and

6. This anonymous and naïve picture from the late sixteenth century, painted on the back of a reused wooden panel and found during minor restoration of the offices of Canterbury Cathedral in 1978, is thought to depict George Babcotte performing at the funeral of Sir Philip Sidney. Though the codpiece has been crudely painted out, you can still see the long black ribbon tied around it, which was the unequivocal symbol of the Funerary Violinist in the London of the 1580s. Close examination also reveals the prosthetic nose. Behind him you can see what many suggest is the black wing of the Angel of Death; however, the missing parts of the panel have not yet been recovered so this hypothesis remains little more than speculation. It is also apparent that the artist had not seen a violin close up as the instrument painted seems to be a cross between a lute and a viol, both of which were much more familiar at the time.

John Rushbey, of whom we know very little. But it is the honorary members who prove most interesting, and indicate both Babcotte's social circle, and the regard in which he was held. These include Edward de Vere, John Lyly, Christopher Marlowe, William Byrd, John Dowland, Tom Watson (marked 'died 1592'), Henry Percy, Thomas Nashe, Thomas Morley and William Shakespeare.

Throughout the 1590s Babcotte's reputation increased at court, and it is thought by some that he became a favourite of the Queen, who was said to like his 'rough and ready manners' and the many pranks he would play involving the 'removal and amusing misplacement' of his nose. This was Babcotte's heyday. He had fame, respect, a £10 pension from De Vere, and an annual salary of £50 for his services to the Heralds of the College of Arms. But status and security were always fragile at this time, and the turn of the century brought a change of fortune for Babcotte. Within seven years he would see all of his major patrons die and his own name fall into disrepute; he would be labelled a heretic and traitor; and his suicide in 1607, whilst fleeing from a warrant of arrest, would lead to an unceremonious burial at a Sussex crossroads (with a stake through his heart).

The last few years of Elizabeth's reign were treacherous ones. With no heir to the throne, nobles and politicians were regrouping, old allegiances were failing and, following the death of many of his patrons, Babcotte found himself increasingly isolated. The Queen was now weakened by age, her mood was not good, and Babcotte's famously grotesque sense of humour was falling out of favour. Though it is impossible to know for sure, records of his performances seem to be far less frequent during this period, and those that we have suggest he may have fallen out with the Heralds, as in 1601 his salary was withdrawn, and there are no longer any accounts of his performing at the funerals of nobility, though he is mentioned in association with a few of his literary friends (he performed at the funerals of Edmund Spenser (1599), Thomas Nashe (1601), Edward de Vere (1604) and John Lyly (1606)).

The year 1603 brought the death of the Queen on 24 March, and a surprising, though brief, return to favour for Babcotte, as he was paid the princely sum of £10 for leading the 'violin bande' at the funeral of the monarch on 28 April. The most likely reason for his momentary reinstatement is the excessive expenditure on the funeral itself. In an attempt to win the favour of the people, King James had authorised an expenditure of over £11,000 for this lavish farewell, pulling out all the stops, and that included Babcotte. (The usual expense for heraldic funerals of the most noble in the land was closer to £3,000.) The band consisted of six musicians, including Peter and Joseph Lupo, sons of Ambrose. However, it seems Babcotte was not permitted to lead the coffin, as had become traditional. There are, unfortunately, no accounts of what was played, and since this is the only known record of Babcotte's performing with other musicians, we are left with the tantalising possibility that the music may have been written down, but no actual answers to this much debated question.

However, in early May of that year Babcotte made the mistake that was ultimately to cost him both his reputation and his life. The are many and varying accounts of the story, and I present here a brief and combined summary.

> On the evening of 2nd May [3rd, 5th, 6th], Babcotte was drinking wine at the house of John Lyly, with ? [a combination of Thomas Nashe, Ludovic Harwoode, John Knowles, Robert Crooke, and James Frederick are cited in various accounts] when a messenger from the king arrived to speak with him. This messenger passed Babcotte a letter bearing the royal seal, which contained a request [demand, summons] that he perform as second violin in the coronation band for a fee of £5. Babcotte's now infamous and celebrated reply was: 'Does your king not know that I only play for the dead, and I drink with the living. I will not play for the living until I drink with the dead!' Whereupon the company laughed. The messenger asked if that was his final answer, and then politely left.

We can only imagine what prompted this most impolitic of answers: whether it was his apparent demotion in the court orchestra, his dislike of the Scottish king, or merely drunken bravura. Nor do we know the king's response upon receiving the reply, but we can be certain that it contributed to Babcotte's falling from grace. In June 1603 the Guild of Funerary Violinists had its royal warrant withdrawn, and was quickly forced underground (the first of many such periods of political hostility and persecution).

Ironically, however, it was another of King James's changes to funerary tradition that enabled Babcotte to continue his work for a further three years. King James, being a Scot, did not approve of England's elaborate heraldic funerals, particularly for the minor nobility, and made some efforts to lesson the influence of the Heralds of the College of Arms. He encouraged his Scottish noblemen to conduct night burials, without the taint of heraldry, and later King James himself sanctioned nocturnal burial by reburying his mother, Mary, Queen of Scots, at night by candlelight, in Westminster Abbey in 1612.

The few accounts we have of Babcotte's last years suggest that he returned to his home town of Canterbury, took on a number of apprentices, and regularly performed at these nocturnal rites, the main source of information being a table of fees in the churchwarden's accounts for St Mary's Church, Canterbury, dated 1605:

> *The Minister's Fees for St Mary's, Canterbury, viz. :–*
> *For Easter offering two pence for all who are above sixteen.*
> *For Churching of Women – six pence.*
> *For Burying with a coffin – 2 shillings*
> *Without a coffin – 1 shilling*
> *For Funeral Sermons, by day – ten shillings*
> *For Funeral Sermons, by night – sixteen shillings*
> *For Babcotte's customary dirges, by night – ten shillings*
> *For Funerary Violin by an apprentice, by day or night – two shillings*
> *For Marrying – five shillings and sixpence*
> *For a commemoration on St John's Day – one Mark*

We also know that Babcotte performed at the (daytime) funerals of his friends Edward de Vere (1604) and John Lyly (1606) 'by special request'.

It is not known whether it was his performance at the funeral of Lyly that prompted the king's anger, or some other indiscretion, or maybe even old enemies whispering in the king's ear, but on 22 November 1606 a warrant was issued for his arrest on charges of treason and heresy. Despite considerable research on the part of scholars, the details of these charges have not so far been established. It seems Babcotte went into hiding for nearly two months, but on the night of 16 January 1607, as the king's soldiers closed in, he took his own life, rather than fall into their hands, by 'falling upon his sword'. As was customary at the time, his suicidal death deprived him of all funerary rights, and he was buried in an unmarked grave, with a stake through his heart, at the meeting of three roads, near Devil's Dyke, Sussex.

Postscript

As is often the case with great men who live through tumultuous times, a number of myths soon arose after Babcotte's death with regard to the final disposal of his body. There are two that have proved to be particularly persistent.

It has frequently been suggested that after his burial his apprentices, led by John Fawlke, dug up his body by night, pulled the stake from his heart, and carefully removed his bowel in one piece. This was then spun into twenty-five sets of violin strings, which, it is alleged, were kept in 'a secrete place' by the remaining members of the Guild 'for purposes of greate ceremony'. Many scholars believe that some of these sets of strings are still in the possession of the Guild, and are played upon only at the funeral of Guild presidents. The Guild of Funerary Violinists declines to comment upon these rumours at the present time.

Another unsubstantiated and frequently unspoken rumour suggests that his finely wrought nose was also taken from the body, and was embellished with a carving of the scene that caused his own nose's unfortunate loss. The nose could be seen at the parish church at Rothbury, Northumberland, where it was left for safe-keeping by the Earl of Derwentwater in 1715, before he marched into defeat at the Battle of Preston. It has been suggested that during renovations in the mid-nineteenth century the nose was inexplicably lost (prompting the addition of a lock on the church door), and later turned up in the Guild archives. Again, the Guild declines to comment upon these rumours at the present time.

In addition to the above rumours are a number of claims to literary inspiration that have been made over the years both by Babcotte's followers and, more recently, by scholars. The two that appear to be most credible relate to the theatrical literary circles in which there is no doubt that Babcotte moved.

The first, more modest claim is that Babcotte was the original inspiration for the character of Hortensio in Shakespeare's *The Taming of the Shrew*. The only concrete association we have between Babcotte and Shakespeare is the list of honorary guild members, though his fame suggests that he was undoubtedly known by Shakespeare if not in person then by reputation. But if one considers there to be any validity in the claim that Edward de Vere was the most likely author of Shakespeare's plays (the fifteenth edition (1975) of the *Encyclopaedia Britannica* states that 'Edward de Vere became in the twentieth century the strongest candidate proposed for the authorship of Shakespeare's plays') then the case seems much stronger. However, there are also a series of documents in the Guild's archives that strongly suggest that William Shakespeare was himself the author of the plays. These papers, dated 1611, which refer to a dispute between the company of the Globe Theatre and the Guild of Funerary Violinists, refer specifically to a number of the later plays, and include a letter purporting to be in Shakespeare's own hand, demanding repayment of fees for services inadequately rendered and threatening court action. They are currently in the hands of eminent Shakespeare scholar Peter Franks, who has requested that we refer to them only in passing, if at all, until their authenticity has been verified.

The other claim is that Babcotte was the inspiration for the main character of Ludovicio in Marlowe's lost play *The Peacock and the Fiddler.* This claim was first cited on paper by Michael Drayton in 1623, and repeated by many, including Dr Johnson. As yet the play remains lost, but if it is found we may get a much more vivid glimpse of the personality of Babcotte himself.

* * * * *

In 1695, the Guild of Funerary Violinists was presented with the letter from Tom Watson to Henry Percy by Percy's heir, the then Earl of Northumberland. Previously unknown, it caused something of a sensation amongst the Guild committee, and at the instigation of its then president, Philip Pope, each member was commissioned to write a piece in the imagined style of their illustrious founder, following closely the form and tone as described by Watson. Tragically, because of repression by the Catholic Church in the Great Funerary Purges of the 1830s and 1840s, most references to this collection were either seized or destroyed, but it can be assumed that there were contributions from Pope himself, Thomas Dinsley, Richard Pocock, Robert Southerland, Alfred Quimby, and doubtless many others.

After the burning of the Guild offices on 22 February 1841, in which its then president, Charles Sudbury, perished, the acting secretary, Matthew Connisten, searched the embers for any salvageable material from the archives, and found, amongst various other papers, the title page for *The Erroneous Dirges of George Babcotte,* and the first piece in the set, by Thomas Dinsley.

The piece is remarkably faithful to Watson's description, and is indeed a worthy composition in its own right, although the language is clearly that of the mid-Baroque and not the Renaissance. It is reminiscent of their more famous German contemporary Heinrich Ignaz Biber, and specifically his *Passacaglia for Solo Violin* (c. 1674), which Biber himself acknowledged was inspired by the Funerary Violin tradition. What sets it apart from similar music of the period is the use of time signature changes to increase the intensity, as described by Watson, and this is beautifully executed by Dinsley, with no sense of contrivance or clumsiness.

The survival of this one piece only serves to highlight the great tragedy of what was lost in the purges, and makes us wonder all the more about the genius of George Babcotte, who single-handedly created what was to become a great tradition, and a unique genre of musical expression. Not only was he the founder of the Guild of Funerary Violinists, an organisation that has now survived for over 400 years despite many attempts to repress and destroy it over its long history; he was also the first of many musicians to recognise the spiritual intention behind performance to the dead. Many times over, cults would arise that took Funerary Violin as the focal point for contact and intercession on behalf of the dead. This single piece is the closest we will ever come to understanding the boldness of that first step: a step born out of the superstitions of the Middle Ages but looking forward to the individualism of the Romantic era. There is no doubt that George Babcotte was indeed a man set apart and, like many of his friends and contemporaries, a man who laid the very foundations for the culture in which we live today.

The Birth of a Tradition

In other times or circumstances, Babcotte's death in 1607 might have spelled the end of what was, after all, still largely one man's vision. But, as we have seen, George Babcotte was a cunning politician, and during his many years of favour at court he was evidently sowing the seeds of both his and his art's future. The early seventeenth century was a period of great upheaval and social change: wealth and power were on the move; old families of influence were being condemned, just as new ones slunk into the vacuum; nothing was secure as England lurched towards the murder of a king; and politicians on both sides saw great advantage and usefulness in seizing the reins of Babcotte's art.

Babcotte had always been less interested in religion itself than in what it could do for him, and it is clear that amongst the apprentices he trained in his later years there were those of both Catholic and Protestant allegiances. Although, of course, he couldn't have known the extent of the social chaos and disorder that was soon to spread across Europe in the wake of the Reformation, with the Thirty Years War and the English Civil War, it was this religious ambiguity that ultimately led to the integration of his art into the funerary rituals not only of England but also of France and the Habsburg Empire (which at the time included today's Croatia, Hungary, Austria, Germany, Italy and Spain), for in the seventy years following his death, politicians on both sides were to use his legacy in the service of their own causes. The Catholics, who perceived his death not as a suicide but as a political and religious martyrdom, embraced Funerary Violin as a vehicle for resistance in the face of Protestant repression. To the Protestants, whose intentions were to rid

Europe of the corrupt superstitious medievalism they perceived in Catholic ritual, Funerary Violin was a perfect puritanical replacement for the many intercessory Catholic funerary rituals that symbolised everything they so despised about the old church.

Throughout the recorded history of our art and culture, there are many examples of the sudden unexpected spread of a new idea or style right across the western world within a remarkably short period of time. So it was with the Renaissance redefining of man in God's image; with the classical and rococo styles of the eighteenth century; and more recently, with the spread of the blues music of the Mississippi delta, which was unknown outside its home in 1900, but by 1970 was the basis of most pop and rock music around the world. There have been many theories proposed as to how and why this happens, but most are agreed that sometimes the evolution of society leaves certain aspects behind, creating holes in man's current expression of himself, and when the right idea comes along to fit that hole the spread is virtually instantaneous (in historical terms). And so it was with Funerary Violin: within two generations of George Babcotte's death, the Art was wholly integrated into the funerary traditions of most of Europe.

In England, Babcotte was succeeded by Thomas Lupo Sr, grandson of the long-lived Ambrose Lupo, Babcotte's one-time enemy, from whom Babcotte's father had stolen the violin in 1542. Thomas Sr remained in the post until 1619, when he was granted the newly created position of Composer to the Violins. He was succeeded by his cousin, also called Thomas Lupo, and thereafter the official records are missing until the end of the Protectorate in 1660. However, two documents have been discovered that shed some light on the Art during this period. The first is a letter recently unearthed in the archive department of Holborn Local Studies Library. Written in 1642 by Thomas Buck, a London printer based in Holborn, and addressed to an unknown man named Jonathan Frith, it describes a funerary performance by Andrew Godestone, at the midnight funeral of Peter Cleeve. It is written in Latin, and further encrypted using a simple displacement code, since it describes a funerary performance in which melodies from the Catholic liturgy were woven into the music as references only those who had attended secret (and illegal) Catholic services would recognise:

> *The violin was played by Andrew Godestone, who claims to have been an apprentice to Babcotte himself, and certainly his playing owes much to the great man whom I had the honour and joy of hearing when in my youth. A finer accompaniment to the moon and stars could not have been envisaged,*

as his playing was full of the mysteries of Creation; of Life and Death; of God's own obscurities. And dear Peter would have been deeply moved to hear those melodies, so familiar to all among us whose loyalties have remained with the Old Church, performed in public as though there were no danger in it, whilst many whose Faith resides with the King, stood by unawares. To us, those words, denied by men whose power resides in this world alone, could not but help to be brought to mind as the melodies wove their way through all that is ancient and good:

> *Dies irae, dies illa,*
> *Solvet saeclum in favilla:*
> *Teste David cum Sibylla.*
>
> *Quantus tremor est futurus,*
> *Quando judex est venturus,*
> *Cuncta stricte discussurus!*
>
> *Tuba mirum spargens sonum*
> *Per sepulcra regionum,*
> *Coget omnes ante thronum …*

To those among us who had ears to hear, not a word was missed, not a phrase out of place, and each declared amid a stream of effortless ornamentation that was worn, like a mask, before the real intent. How cleverly he bent our ears to sacred rites unspoken, and left us in mind of the Requiems of old, before these dark days in which we are fated to live. And yet none who stand with the King's own blasphemy could hear a single word of it. [decoded and partially translated from the original Latin]

History has shown many times over that when words are banned the other arts take on their mantel, and music, which is the most difficult of all the arts to pin to a standard, often becomes the symbol through which otherwise illegal ideas can be expressed, so long as only those in the know can recognise them. This letter was written at a time when participating in a Catholic Mass was potentially punishable by death, and clearly demonstrates just such a subversive use of music.

The other illuminating document is an unofficial letter written by John Howson, Bishop of Oxford, to Richard Corbet, Dean of Christ Church, in 1624. The majority of the letter is of no interest, dealing as it does with issues of church budgets and internal policy. It is in the fourth paragraph, in which Corbet speaks of the suppression of Puritanism, that a single, though telling, reference is made to the Art. He says simply:

Babcotte's followers are to be encouraged, as their activities have proven to be of great help in these matters. [translated from the original French]

This single sentence has aroused more debate amongst scholars of the history of Funerary Violin than possibly any other single sentence ever written. Indeed it very nearly caused a split within the Guild of Funerary Violinists itself in 1871. The main issue of contention is what exactly is meant by the word 'activities'. Today it is largely accepted that the word refers exclusively to their expected funerary activities, but some have suggested that it implies a more active political participation in events of the time. The words 'Babcotte's followers' are themselves revealing as they imply that nearly twenty years after his death Babcotte was seen not as a mere musician but as some kind of spiritual leader, whose followers were a describable unit, sublimated in the act of following Babcotte (it has been suggested by some that the sentence refers to a different Babcotte, and has nothing to do with Funerary Violin whatsoever – though this view has now, in the eyes of the Guild, been thoroughly discredited). However the statement is interpreted, it is clear that the Church was encouraging the spread of the Art, albeit for its own political reasons, and this is likely to have been of major assistance in its integration into general funerary practice across England.

After Babcotte's death a number of his Catholic apprentices fled England in fear of the many further persecutions meted out by James I against the Old Faith, and were ultimately welcomed into France, the Habsburg territories and the Holy Roman Empire, establishing Funerary Violin as a tradition throughout western Europe. Unfortunately, during the hundreds of years of chaos and conflict across Europe that followed, many of the early records of this first great flourish of the Art of Funerary Violin were lost, and much of that which survived was then either seized or destroyed during the Great Funerary Purges of the 1830s and 1840s; but a handful of references have survived, mainly amongst various forms of governmental records, which demonstrate the spread of the art, in most cases simply consisting of a name, invariably English, and a title, roughly translated as Funerary Violinist to the court/parish/district.

There is further evidence of the arrival of Funerary Violin in Spain in a painting by El Greco, thought to have been completed in 1609, which hangs on the wall in the vestibule of the Church of Santo Tome in Toledo, Spain. Entitled *The Burial of Count Orgaz,* the painting originally included a clear depiction of an unknown Funerary Violinist. However, the church was closed for refurbishment in the summer of 1839, and upon its reopening eighteen months later it was noted, by some, that the Funerary Violinist had been carefully and cleverly painted out of the picture, having been retouched into the image of a cowled monk. Close examination still suggests a violinist's posture, but were it not for a sketch of the original made in 1780 by Nathaniel Edgcombe (tragically now lost), this historical deception might have passed unnoticed. That the painting included a Funerary Violinist at all clearly indicates the early integration of Funerary Violin into Spanish funeral rites.

For almost thirty-five years after the death of George Babcotte, the history of Funerary Violin reveals little but a handful of names and places with no further evidence to colour the picture. It is not until 1641, with the emergence of Bulstrode Whycherley amongst the entourage of Prince Rupert of the Rhine, that a character appears whose impact on society is so great that, even today, he is remembered in folk songs and stories, although it is true that many who repeat these tales have no idea of his importance as a hero of the Civil War, nor even of his profession. To them he is merely a name in a song.

Bulstrode Whycherley

and Prince Rupert of the Rhine

7. Prince Rupert pictured in 1644. During his time
in England he adopted the English fashion for the
long periwig, a fashion he soon abandoned after
his exile in 1646.

Nothing whatever is known about Bulstrode Whycherley before 1641, when it is
thought he arrived in England amidst the military entourage of Prince Rupert of the
Rhine, and indeed very little is known about him thereafter save for a handful of
documents, mainly referring to him in the context of Civil War battles.

Prince Rupert himself was an extraordinary man, whose tremendous success as a military commander in his youth was balanced by the great scientific achievements of his later life. He experimented not only in the military applications of chemistry (such as new techniques for boring barrels or mixing gunpowder, and the invention of a new form of brass known as Prince's metal) but also in the techniques of mezzotint engraving, which he introduced to England in 1660, and he was a founder member of the Royal Society. It is therefore of little surprise that he was the first to have the imagination and insight to see the many potential military applications of Funerary Violin.

Prince Rupert was born in Prague on 17 December 1619, the third son of Charles I's sister Elizabeth, the 'Winter Queen', by her marriage to Frederick V, Elector of the Palatinate. In 1620, during the Thirty Years War, the family was driven into exile in Holland, where Rupert grew up, though he visited England in 1636 and became a favourite of his uncle, King Charles I, and Queen Henrietta Maria. Rupert became a soldier at the age of fourteen, fighting for the Protestant Prince of Orange at the sieges of Rheinberg (1633) and Breda (1637), but in 1638, during an invasion of Westphalia, he was captured by Imperial forces and held prisoner at Linz in Austria for nearly three years. It is thought by many scholars that he met Bulstrode Whycherley whilst in captivity, as Whycherley's name first appears in a list of the Prince's entourage in 1641, after he was released on condition that he would never again bear arms against the Emperor.

The outbreak of the Civil War in England presented Rupert with an opportunity to continue his military career, and in August 1642 he and his younger brother, Prince Maurice, arrived in England accompanied by a staff of English and Scottish veterans from the European wars, including Bulstrode Whycherley, to fight for King Charles.

The earliest mention of Whycherley's playing is an eye-witness account of the moments before the Battle of Edgehill (23 October 1642), related by a Royalist foot soldier, Richard Pruwet, to Thomas Godestone, a man with literary aspirations, two days after the event:

> *We were all afeared of the outcome. Arms were the great deficiency, and we stood in the same garments in which we left our native fields, with scythes, pitchforks, and even sickles in our hands. There was a grim silence as none of us dared to speak, and as we stared across the field at our very enemy,*

Prince Rupert gave the command to Whycherley, and he took up his violin. This dirgeful music, well known and beloved of the Dead, cut through the silence like a sword, preparing and consoling us for the inevitable slaughter, and when he ceased we cheerfully took to the field and, literally like reapers, descended to the Harvest of Death.

Though never specifically referred to as a Funerary Violinist, accounts such as this one make it clear that even the foot soldiers were well aware of the mortal associations of his playing, and so, in the opinion of the author, it is fair to assume he was indeed a Funerary Violinist. This is the earliest direct mention of Whycherley's role, but there is a rather tantalising mention of him that appeared twenty years later, in a collection of ballads entitled *Rump Songs*, published in London in 1662, though it relates to the earlier Battle of Powick Bridge (23 September 1642), considered the first major military action of the Civil War. Entitled 'Battel of Worcester', and intended to be sung to the tune of 'Green Sleeves', or 'Which Nobody', this ballad contains a surprisingly detailed account of the battle, though I quote it only up to the mention of Whycherley:

> *All you that be true to the King & the State,*
> *Come listen, and Ile tell you what happen'd of late,*
> *In a large field near Worcesters gate,*
> *Which no body can deny.*
> *Brave Sir John Byron, true to the Crown,*
> *With forces too few 'tis very well known,*
> *Went thither 'tis said, to keep the Town,*
> *Which no body can deny.*
>
> *But whether 'twas true, ye have learn'd to guess,*
> *As for my own part I think no lesse,*
> *To give you a taste of our Future successe,*
> *Which no body can deny.*
> *Thither came Fines with armes Complete,*
> *The Town to take, and Byron defeat,*
> *Provisions were made, but he staid not to eat,*
> *Which no body can deny.*
>
> *But as soone as he hear'd Old Whycherley play,*
> *With a flea in's ear, he ran quite away,*
> *For the dirges inton'd his defeat that day,*

Which no body can deny.
Nay had the old Crop-ear'd his Father dar'd
To approach the walls, his design had bin marr'd,
For Byron would not have proved a Ward,
Which no body, &c. ...

This ballad, which goes on to mention all the major persons and events of the battle, is interesting for two reasons. First, that Whycherley is named at all suggests that by the time the ballad was written he had become a popular folk hero for the Royalists, and that his exploits were well enough known, and considered to be of great enough importance, to make him worthy of mention. Second, if the order of events in the ballad is to be taken literally – and many key events in the ballad are corroborated by other documents – we can assume Whycherley's role was the same in this battle as in the later Battle of Edgehill. If this is the case, it could be strongly suggested that the first shots fired in the English Civil War were fired, not by cannon or musket, but by the sonorous tones of a Funerary Violinist.

Another eye-witness account of Whycherley's ability to inspire comes from Edmund Verney, a Royalist officer, in a letter to his son written both before and after the battle of Newbury (19 and 20 September 1643):

Our men are very raw, our victuals scarce and provisions for horses worse. I dare say there was never so raw, so unskilful and so unwilling an army brought to fight. Were it not for Whycherley's dirges I wonder if the men would stand at all, for it is his doleful performance that reminds us all of the solemnity of the causes for which we fight and prepare to die ...

And, later in the same letter, after the battle:

The field was covered with the dead, yet no one could tell to what party they belonged, nor whether they died noble deaths, or passed unto Heaven through the coward's gate, for surely some on both sides did extremely well, and others did ill and deserved to be hanged. The smell of death was all about, and the field itself seemed red with the endless streams of blood spilt by brother upon brother, cousin upon cousin. It seemed almost a vision of Hell itself, until I caught the distant strains of Whycherley, who had taken up position on the hill, and played upon his violin to sooth the dead; and in my heart I know he played for both us and them, Royalists and Parliamentarians,

Roundheads and Cavaliers, and it seemed to me that there was, after all, still hope for Man, even in this God-forsaken Hell of his own making ...

We know that Whycherley was seriously wounded in the aftermath of the Battle of Nantwich, on 25 January 1644, as Dr William Harvey, a surgeon in the Royalist army, who found him the next morning, later recounted the story in his (as yet unpublished) journal:

I came upon Bulstrode Whycherley, who was dangerously wounded, and had been left amongst the dead men. The local people had stripped him, which helped to save his life. It was cold clear weather, and a frost that night, which staunched his bleeding, and about midnight, or some hours after his hurt, he awakened and was forced to draw a dead body upon him for warmth ...

We can assume that he recovered from his injuries, as the next, and final, mention of him is six months later, in a record of the dead after the Battle of Marston Moor, on 24 July 1644. Though we cannot be certain that the name refers to him, as Bulstrode Whycherley was not an uncommon name at the time (as is evidenced by the fact that two Bulstrode Whycherleys are recorded as killed during the battle), there are no further mentions of him thereafter, and he is no longer listed amongst Prince Rupert's men.

Tantalising though these accounts are, they only cover a period of three years, and are so fragmentary that it is impossible to get a real picture of the man. He clearly had a unique symbolic and spiritual role amongst Prince Rupert's men, and was held in high regard, at least by those who left written accounts. But the most alluring question of all, that of what it was that he played, can never be known as no written music by him has ever been found, and it is most likely that he was improvising, or playing pieces that he had either learnt or composed himself, from memory. He remains an enigma, unique in the so far discovered history of Funerary Violin, as the only Funerary Violinist to become, not just a symbol of hope and humanity in a deplorable period of war, but a military weapon in his own right.

During the Commonwealth that followed, Oliver Cromwell spread absolute Puritanism about the land, and Funerary Violin was amongst the many arts that were banned outright. Whether it was continued in secret during this dark period in English history is not known at present, since no records have been found, although if it did it persist it is likely that no records would have been kept, as punishment was both swift and brutal for any transgressions of the new religious laws.

8. This image of Bulstrode Whycherley was widely circulated after the Restoration. In 1661 he was given a posthumous knighthood by Charles II, which brought him once again to the attention of the popular imagination and made of him a symbol of the marriage between Art, War, Death and Loyalty: all major concerns of Restoration England. Painted in 1662, a full eighteen years after his death, the picture quite probably bears little, if any, resemblance to the man himself, but served more as an idealised representation of how he might, or should, have looked. (Sadly, the original is lost, and this etching, dated 1806, is the only surviving copy.)

With the Restoration of the monarchy in 1660, Charles II created a new official post of Master of the King's Funerary Violinists for Compton Walberswick, who had been amongst his entourage during his years in exile. There is, amongst the archives of the Guild of Funerary Violinists, a single hand-written score by Compton Walberswick. Entitled 'Funerary Processional' and dated 1682, it is amongst the very earliest known written examples of the form, and is therefore of considerable historical interest, although, it must be admitted that musically it is very weak, and is possibly the poorest piece of Funerary Violin music to remain in the repertoire.

Herbert Stanley Littlejohn

and the Canterbury Funerary Suites

9. Herbert Stanley Littlejohn, photographed in 1956.

In November 1954 Daniel Haughton, a young musicologist, had come to Chichester Cathedral to further his research into seventeenth-century English church music, and noticed on a shelf in the private library – the first man to have done so for nearly 200 years – a hand-written book of music, copied by Father John Brockley in 1726, entitled *Various Works for the Performance of Funerary Violin.* On its title page there was glued a print, obviously cut from some other contempo-

48

raneous publication, of a violinist, underneath which was written, in Brockley's hand, 'Charles Montesquieu, Surintendant des Violonistes Funèbres du Roi'. The book contained a suite by Orlando Addleston dated 1681, a suite by Michel Meunier dated 1693, and a suite by Kaspar Ignaz Faustmann dated 1722, each of them with three movements, and each with its own title and subtitle. By chance, where a lesser scholar might have passed over such a find as not relevant to his specialism, Haughton had known Herbert Stanley Littlejohn at Oxford (Littlejohn was two years his senior) and had remained in touch, and so knew of Funerary Violin and recognised the tremendous importance of this find.

Herbert Stanley Littlejohn was born in 1929, and educated at Wells Cathedral School. After his National Service he took a degree in music and theology at Oxford University before starting what might have become a successful career in music criticism. In 1954 he was elected Acting Secretary to the Guild of Funerary Violinists, which at the time was reduced to little more than a gentlemen's club for amateur musicians. With the discovery of the Chichester manuscripts a few months later he was naturally extremely excited, and was keen to be amongst the first to study them. Haughton and Littlejohn spent the next three months examining the manuscripts meticulously, authenticating the chemical construction of the ink, and were finally satisfied as to the genuine date of the book being 1726. They were further convinced that Father John Brockley, the copyist, believed the pieces to have been composed specifically for the tradition of Funerary Violin, making them amongst the earliest written examples of Funerary Violin yet discovered. (Until the early eighteenth century Funerary Violin was an improvised tradition, and it was not until its imitation was hijacked by court composers in France, to great acclaim, as the *Tombeau* that Funerary Violinists slowly began to see the advantages of composing specific written-out works.)

In November 1956, two years after their discovery, Littlejohn arranged through Donald Whitley, a friend who worked for Parlophone Records, to make a set of recordings of the newly discovered works over the Christmas break, when their small studio at Shepherds Bush would be empty and equipment could be borrowed. The recordings were to be made between 27 and 30 December in a large private house in Dulwich with a famously fine acoustic, and were going well until the evening of 28 December, when Littlejohn tripped over an elderly cat and fell down the stairs, breaking his neck and fracturing his skull. He died of his injuries on 12 January 1957, leaving two of the pieces unrecorded. The recordings that had been completed were pressed on vinyl by Whitley and presented to the Guild of Funerary Violinists at Littlejohn's funeral service (it is said that, though no violinist played at the service itself, a number of Guild members gathered by his grave that night to perform the requisite works). Strangely, Haughton himself was dead before the end of March 1957 (after a prolonged high fever with vomiting) and the original manuscript has not been seen since. Thankfully, the men had both made detailed copies.

Nothing whatever is known about the three composers represented, as thorough research has so far revealed no further references to them in state, church or council records, though there remains more work to be done. Their names suggest nationalities that are further represented in the styles of the relevant suites, but whether they were composed in England, presented in England or merely brought to England in manuscript form is unknown. The pieces are titled and subtitled as follows:

Orlando Addleston
Funerarius for Michael Wise Esquire,
    Musician, Philosopher and Horologist (1681)
I.   *Grave*
II.   *Andante con moto*
III.   *Allegretto*

Michel Meunier
Pompes Funèbres no. 2 (1693)
I.   *Pompe I*
II.   *Pompe II*
III.   *Pompe II*

Kaspar Ignaz Faustmann
Todesmusik (1722)
I.   *Intrada*
II.   *Trauermarsch I*
III.   *Trauermarsch II*

The music is not untypical of the period, being similar in many respects to courtly instrumental and dance pieces, though of a more sombre character, but it is quite unlike the descriptions of improvised funerary performances that have survived, leaving many questions unanswered. If these are genuine works of Funerary Violin, they may have been composed to emulate the success of the *Tombeau,* and

10. Charles Montesquieu?
Surintendant des Violonistes
Funèbres du Roi?

so have tamed many of the more earthly excesses of emotion that are so often referred to. Of course, it could be that Fr Brockley was simply mistaken in his classification, but the pieces seem too appropriate for this to be mere chance; or it could be that they are simply a forgery, in which case were they forged by Fr Brockley in 1726? And if so, what was his motive? Was he covering up his own compositions, of which he knew the church would disapprove? Or were they forged more recently for Haughton to find?

Of late, some scholars have even suggested that these works were possibly a prank perpetrated upon Littlejohn by Haughton, citing some uncontemporaneous harmonies as their evidence, though others have posited that a greater knowledge of the Funerary Violin tradition would make them aware of the unusual mix of modal and harmonic elements that so characterised the music of Funerary Violinists. In the 1970s more credence was given to the manuscript by the discovery of six suites for solo bass viol by Monsieur de Sainte Colombe le Fils, two pieces of which have some subtly striking fragmentary melodic similarities with Pompes II and III by Michel Meunier, which raises new issues, but does suggest (in the opinion of the author) that the pieces, which have become known as the 'Chichester Funerary Suites', are indeed genuine works, though by whom it is impossible to be certain.

The performances recorded by Herbert Stanley Littlejohn are typical of the period in their gusto and stridency, and Littlejohn himself was renowned amongst

11. By the early 1700s the Art of Funerary Violin was well established and had spread from the court to villages all over England, with variable degrees of success in terms of both artistry and intention. Initially in many cases it was the village fiddler who took on the role, with little or no knowledge of the true and valid repertoire, leading many critics to deplore the inappropriate and at times scandalous lack of gravity they brought to the proceedings. Often accused of turning the funerary ritual into nothing short of a party, and the congregation into a rabble, these peasant Funerary Violinists were frequently parodied by cartoonists of the time. This etching, one a series of twelve designed by William Hogarth and entitled 'The Funeral Procession', is just such a critique. Whilst they are rich in the typical symbolism of the day, perhaps the most telling point is the lack of a coffin: Hogarth is suggesting that the Funerary Violinist has so raised the hackles of the assembled crowd that they have forgotten the deceased altogether, and are more concerned with an argument with a passing gentlemen and his squire. To further deprive the Funerary Violinist of dignity, he has been portrayed with only one leg, making him readily associated with the many beggars that populated the streets of London at the time. The sticks of hawthorn being waved by the crowd were traditionally carried as part of the Somerset funeral rite, and symbolised the regenerative power of nature, after the myth of Joseph of Arimathea, who is said to have thrust his staff into the ground of Wearyall Hill, near Glastonbury, where it took root and grew into a thorn tree.

members of the Guild, amateur musicians to a man, for his playing's 'ceaseless enthusiasm and undeniable volume', both of which are much in evidence in these recordings, though at times perhaps a little inappropriately. There are occasional issues with tuning, the odd mistake, and subtle rearrangements in terms of both pitches and structure, which are all entirely in keeping with the Funerary Violin

12. This funeral ticket, again designed by William Hogarth, dated 1720 and commissioned by the undertaker Humphrey Drew, illustrates in a more subtle way Hogarth's dislike of Funerary Violinists, and specifically a dislike of Jebediah Bott, Funerary Violinist to George I, with whom he had fallen out in 1718, allegedly over a woman. Commissioned to demonstrate all the funerary pomp that Drew had to offer (and Drew often employed Bott), Hogarth was obliged to include a Funerary Violinist in the picture, specifically Jebediah Bott, despite his many personal objections to the Art and that particular practitioner. At the time it was traditional for the Funerary Violinist to lead the funeral procession, thus making him the first to enter the church, and Hogarth takes full advantage of this moment to depict Bott disappearing into the shadows of the church, making him present but barely visible. Close examination reveals a further snub: he has portrayed Bott as left-handed (the bow can be seen appearing over his right shoulder), a trait that was, at the time associated with various forms of mental imbalance and spiritual decadence.

tradition, but his commitment and vigour are undeniable, making the tragedy of his sudden, unexpected death during the recordings all the more poignant.

Regardless of the quality of the playing, these recordings remain of immense historic and musical interest as they are, to this day, the only recording of these works ever made. In addition, they are a personal memorial to Herbert Stanley Littlejohn, and a testament to the poor standard of technical performance amongst Guild members in what remains one of our darkest periods.

John (Jane) Pemberton

A Sheep in Wolf's Clothing

John (Jane) Pemberton would have been completely forgotten had it not been for a curious article that appeared in the *London Evening Post* on 17 March 1802, entitled 'A Strange Story':

> *An incident is just now being discussed in musical circles so extraordinary that, were not the truth capable of being vouched for by official authority, the narration would certainly be deemed incredible. Many members of the Guild of Funerary Violinists, and others of the London funerary professions may recall a certain John Pemberton, Funerary Violinist, attached to the Parish of Holborn, who enjoyed a reputation for considerable skill in his profession, especially for firmness, decision, and rapidity of execution in often difficult circumstances. The said gentleman had first entered the profession in 1769, as an apprentice to the renowned William Snook, and had risen through the rank and file to become First Funerary Violinist to the Parish of Holborn, and an esteemed member of the Guild. His professional acquirements had procured for him a number of honours and he had performed many times for the souls of those worthy of note and celebrity. He died last Sunday of a sudden seizure, due to constriction of the chest (according to the doctor present) whilst executing his professional duties for the departed soul of Edmund Petygard at St George the Martyr, and, upon his death he was found to be A WOMAN! The motives that occasioned and the time when commenced this singular deception are both shrouded in mystery. But it stands as an indisputable fact that a woman was, for 33 years,*

a practising member of the Guild of Funerary Violinists, in the official employ of the British government, fought two duels and had sought many more, had pursued a legitimate qualification from the Guild and received a regular diploma, and acquired almost a celebrity for skill as a Funerary Violinist.

Further research has revealed very little about John Pemberton. As is indicated in the article, his name first appears in the parish records in 1769, and he was given a full post in 1775, and finally rose to the position of First Funerary Violinist for the parish of Holborn in 1785, a post he held until his death in 1802, being paid two half-crowns per funeral at the height of his career, and performing for the souls of the semi-notable middle classes of his day. The parish register records his death as from a 'seizure induced by considerable constriction of the chest during strenuous activity', and it can be speculated that this may have been due to the inevitable tight bandage he must have worn to disguise his apparently ample bosom.

Recent scholarship has suggested that there may be a link between the aforesaid John Pemberton and a certain Jane Pemberton, who is mentioned in the Lambeth court records of 1764, when her widowed mother, Mary Pemberton, was prosecuted for attempting to defraud Laurence Cobbe, her father-in-law, of moneys due for the maintenance of a son. These records indicate that Jane Pemberton was brought up as a boy, with only her mother and herself knowing the truth of her gender, until she reached fourteen, when an alleged sodomitical affair with Daniel Messingham brought the truth into the open. The records also show that Jane Pemberton (known at the time as James) had been apprenticed to William Snook, and showed 'some talent' for Funerary Violin. Assuming that this is the same person, as seems likely, it is interesting to note that 'John Pemberton' was apprenticed to William Snook in 1665, implying that Snook was well aware of both Pemberton's genuine identity and gender, and was therefore a willing accomplice in this unusual case of identity fraud.

John (Jane) Pemberton remains the only woman, as yet discovered, to have held an official post as a Funerary Violinist.

Herr Hieronymous Gratchenfleiss

The Greatest of the Funerary Violinists?

Now long since forgotten, Herr Gratchenfleiss was, in his day, as famous as Paganini, Heifetz or Menuhin. Indeed, not just he, but the whole tradition of Funerary Violin performance, has now passed out of our cultural memory: a testament to the destructive forces that can be unleashed when artistry, politics and religion collide. His tremendous fame, extraordinary virtuosity and tendency towards spiritual self-aggrandisement were to lead, in time, to accusations of demonic pacts and unholy unions. When, shortly after his death in 1810, a cult arose in his name that briefly caught the imagination of all Europe, and a thousand new pretenders were spawned, it was almost inevitable that the Vatican would feel obliged to act in defence of the One True Faith and the sanctity of consecrated ground.

By 1833 the Cult of Funerary Violin had reached its zenith and Pope Gregory XVI, through the efforts of Cardinal Pacca, took action with a fanatical zeal unseen since the Albigensian crusade. This included the wholesale destruction of the Funerary Violin tradition, which stretched back over 300 years, and the subsequent removal of any references to it. Historic records, books and sheet music were all seized; paintings were either burnt or, where necessary, retouched or cropped to remove the offending images; instruments with the traditional death's head scroll were either 'restored' or destroyed; the performers themselves were forced into monastic orders, and in time the entire notion of a Funerary Violinist was forgotten.

Herr Hieronymous Gratchenfleiß

Kurfürstentrauerviolinistenmeister

From an Original Picture in the Possession of J. Bland

13. This etching of Herr Gratchenfleiss was made in 1775, during his visit to London. Possibly as a reaction to the unsympathetic attitude of the English press to his eccentric dress, he has uncharacteristically chosen to be presented in the manner of a classical music performer, dressed in the height of English fashion, rather than his usual late seventeenth-century style of the long periwig and frock coat. It is probably for this reason that the picture was overlooked during the Great Funerary Purges of the 1830s and 1840s and has survived, in the British Library, to this day. The scar clearly visible on his left cheek is thought to have been the result of a duel with Walter Kriebel in 1765. Though the cause of the duel is unknown, records indicate that Kriebel, Funerary Violinist to Duke Charles II of Würtemburg, lost two fingers from his left hand, resulting in an unceremonious end to his career.

It is doubtful whether such repression could have taken place, or such results been achieved, without the support and cooperation of government officials throughout Europe, but so little evidence remains that it is impossible to say (it is thought that the libraries of the Vatican may hold many such seized documents, and maybe one day they will come to light). What little we do know has been painstakingly pieced together from a handful of fragments, and unsubstantiated and often unspoken rumours. Until the recent discovery of these notebooks there was no solid evidence that such a rich tradition had existed at all.

Herr Hieronymous Gratchenfleiss, or Grauschenfleiss (it was on a trip to London in 1775 that he so liked the English mispronunciation of his name that he decided to adopt it), was born in Wolfsburg, Lower Saxony, in 1736. (It is worth mentioning that his insistence on being called 'Herr' Gratchenfleiss was most unusual at the time, if not unheard of, and may have been one of the instances that set the current trend. At the time, in Saxony, official titles were very much in vogue and Herr Gratchenfleiss was making a statement by deriving a title from his own lack of position. It is a testament to his convictions that he continued to use the prefix 'Herr' even when in the employ of the Prince Electors, when he could have used the much more impressive Kurfürstentrauerviolinistenmeister Gratchenfleiss.)

In the mid eighteenth century it was common for the town or village undertaker/carpenter to double as a violinist for festivals and funerals (not weddings, as this was deemed to be bad luck) and Gratchenfleiss came from just such a family. At court the role of the Funerary Violinist as a dedicated specialist was already long established. The young Hieronymous, aged seven, was present at the funeral procession of Gustav Holtsbrunner (a notable banker and friend of the Prince Elector), and saw at first hand the artistry of Kurfürstentrauerviolinistenmeister Schinker, Funerary Violinist to Frederick Augustus II, who led the grand procession. This clearly made a deep impression upon him for, as a result, he turned all his attention to practising the violin, much to the consternation of his father, who considered undertaking to be the more respectable side of the trade.

Little more is known until, at the age of fourteen (in 1750) he became a student of G. K. Bach (a less gifted cousin of the famous J. S.). Under his tuition Gratchenfleiss was exposed to all the latest musical and aesthetic ideas, and it was at this time that many of the radical approaches that led to his becoming the foremost Funerary Violinist of his day, if not of all time, were established. It was also at this time that he first came upon the 'ancient' music of the early seventeenth century, amongst the private collection of his tutor. Years later he was to write in his Testament (found in the now famous Hildesheim trunk):

It was then that I saw the truth of it all; that counterpoint, as extolled and proclaimed by my master Herr Bach, was by now no more than an empty vessel, a formulation that carried within it no more meaning nor value than a quill without ink; its passion long since spent; a cadaver behind which all manner of musical vagabonds and miscreants could hide their own vacuous propensity. Nor did I find the endless harmonic meanderings of my master's more worthy cousin, Johann Sebastian Bach, to be of any great inspiration, wallowing as they did in the falsification of cleverness for its own honour's sake. No, it was to the distant past that I looked; to the works of Schaab, Freidkin and Eisenmenger; to the glorious essays in bold simplicity of Grubel and Haube, to the spiritual vigour of Grupp and Baublitz – in short, to the music of a century earlier, before the twin demons of harmony and counterpoint had devoured what soul there was left in the music of the heart.

It is clear from these few words (unfortunately much of the manuscript was eaten away by mould) that Gratchenfleiss was already striding a previously untrodden path, marrying the stoic discipline and simplicity of late Renaissance and early Baroque music, with the Romanticism and vigour of *Sturm und Drang*. It also helps to make sense of some of his many eccentricities, such as the use of white face make-up and beauty spots for all funerary performances, and the adoption of the seventeenth-century long wig, just as others were discarding the hairpiece altogether.

Again there is a chapter of his life that remains unknown to us until, in 1758, at the age of only twenty-two, he took over the position that had so inspired him as a child: that of Funerary Violinist to the Prince Elector of Saxony, a post he was to hold (officially if not in practice) until his death in 1810. No records remain to catalogue the many funerals he must have performed at, but it can be assumed that these would have included those of all the notables of his day. We do know that by the 1770s he was performing all over Europe to great acclaim. A long-overlooked diary entry was recently brought to light, which gives an indication:

17th January 1772

The Duchess Isabella was laid to rest today. The service took place in the Cathedral and was attended by many noble families and eminent figures. Many of them, I fear, had arrived for the social aspect of the ceremony and,

not having known or loved the deceased as I had, there was a distinct attitude
of subdued gaiety outside the church.

*The Funerary Violinist was a Herr Gratchenfleiss who had come highly
recommended by Count Schlossenburg who had first hand experience of his
expertise having attended the funeral of Duke Ivan III in St Petersburg the
previous spring. Consequently the service was delayed by a week to enable
Herr Gratchenfleiss to make the treacherous journey from Tblisi where he
had played for the Bishop of Rheims who died suddenly after an accident
with a recalcitrant mare ... Herr Gratchenfleiss' melodies pierced the
gloomy air of the dingy chapel and transported the congregation closer to
heaven where the soul of our loved one now resides ...* [taken from *The Diary
of Pieter Von Cusk*, pub. 1843]

A later entry in the same diary presents an interesting if brief portrait of the man:

25th January 1772

*To Frau Volstanger's for dinner at which were gathered many luminaries
including the esteemed Funerary Violin player Herr Gratchenfleiss, who
gave a spirited and eloquent defence of his art in light of recent murmurings
against it by fashionable intellectuals ... Despite the attitude of certain
factions within the Church and the scandalous behaviour of some of the more
outré adherents of the current fashion for chalk-white make-up amongst the
many followers of Funerary Violin players, Herr Gratchenfleiss maintains
that when he performs at a service he is honouring the entire kingdom of the
dead and not merely the deceased person whose friends and relatives have
gathered to inter the unfortunate departed.*

*I'm sure I shall awake with a sore head in the morning which will be penance
enough for the sin of over-imbibance this fine evening. I'm rather thrilled to
have spent this evening with such a noble fellow though and my regret will
be a small one.* [taken from *The Diary of Pieter Von Cusk*]

In 1775 Gratchenfleiss visited London, and though it is not known if this was for
a specific commission or a general tour, we do know that he performed at the
funeral of Sir Alexander Tovy, a high-ranking civil servant, in a grand procession
that concluded with a much talked-about demonstration of funerary passion at the
gates of Westminster Abbey.

By 1780 his aesthetic had evolved into a semi-religious fervour, as is revealed once again by the fragments of the Hildesheim trunk testimony:

One night in the winter of 1780, I was lying in my bed, staring absent-mind-edly at the Death's Head scroll of my violin, so lovingly carved by the great Jacob Steiner in his very prime, when a vision came to me, so distinct and vivid that it could be nothing but the effortless work of God himself. Though it is impossible to describe the wondrous journey that overwhelmed my every sense, the purpose and meaning was entirely clear: that the musical expression of Death was so much more than a mere performance, or even Art, but has a power to open the very door to the Underworld; and that, combined with the flight of the Soul on the third day after death, it can draw the fallen from their everlasting torment down below, and send them, cleansed and purified, back to their rightful place beside our Saviour. No sooner had I grasped the meaning of this ... [the remainder of the document is illegible]

This single paragraph goes a long way towards explaining the nature of the cult that arose after Gratchenfleiss's death, and why it upset the Vatican to such a degree. It also gives us a greater understanding of the workings of the complex mind that not only created the extraordinary works to be found in these notebooks, but also went on to inspire so many white-faced imitators for two whole decades, until the Great Funerary Purges of the 1830s and 1840s brought the whole story to an end.

No further references have been found to Herr Gratchenfleiss in the 1780s, but a tantalising, and now much quoted, letter dated 1797, by an unknown man named Fredrik, has come to light:

14th September 1797

Dear Gretchen,

I am regrettably writing to inform you that your cousin, and my own dear father, has passed away after a long and difficult illness. In many ways his passing was a blessing as the struggle had taken a deep toll on the poor man, and I do not think I could have borne it for much longer. For the service we asked Father Reichelderfer who spoke very beautifully, if a little boldly, and for the customary dirges we employed the renowned Herr Gratchenfleiss, who was most heartily recommended by the Father. Herr Gratchenfleiss proved to be a most difficult and eccentric character, and his demands that the ceremony take place precisely three days after Papa's decease, to the minute, caused much consternation as he had died at three thirty in the morning. In addition, over the few years since the Father had last met with him, he had lost his voice to consumption of the throat which made communication all the more strained through the use of written notes and much gesticulation. By chance the moon was nearly full on the chosen night, and the weather was surprisingly mild. Herr Gratchenfleiss appeared, disconcertingly, in a long frock coat of the old style, a long black wig, and his faced painted a vivid white with the occasional beauty spot, and an elegant sabre hanging at his side. At first it seemed to us that he himself might have risen from one of the many tombs around us, but when he put bow to string all our doubts were allayed. I cannot impress upon you enough how wondrous and appropriate was his playing, and amongst those assembled, myself most earnestly included, no matter how our hearts were weighed with sorrow up until that moment, upon his conclusion, we were all deeply uplifted, and left in no doubt as to the Eternal Peace in which my dear father now walks. He is truly an extraordinary man, and the fee of 20 florins, which we first considered somewhat oversized, now seems to be paltry compared to the tremendous service he has done for our family. Yours most sincerely, Fredrik

This letter gives us a fascinating insight into the increasing eccentricity of Herr Gratchenfleiss in his sixth decade, and the awe and respect he by then inspired. Whether he was genuinely mute by this time is unknown, but a single conversation book has been discovered, in which we have the maestro's half of what *may* have been an interesting exchange:

Always!!!

—

Stuff and nonsense. In my opinion he should be hanged by the testicles.

—

That's hardly enough. I would require at least 100, and of the finest quality!

—

If you insist then I will, as ever, oblige, but under protest.

—

XXXXX

The discourse continues for ten pages, but scholars have yet to unravel the subject matter under discussion as the nature of such notebooks is abrupt and one-sided, and the previously quoted letter suggests that much communication was done via gesticulation.

The only other contemporary reference that has so far come to light is a brief, though telling, obituary that appeared in the Wolfsburg Monatsnachrichten (a pamphlet that was produced monthly between 1806 and 1817):

> *On the last Sunday of April was buried Wolfburg's most honoured and respected son, Herr Hieronymous Gratchenfleiss, the unquestioned master of the Art of Funerary Violin, who bore the official title of Master of His Majesty the Prince Elector's Funerary Violinists for 52 years. Revered throughout Europe for his extraordinary ability to still the Soul with his violin, he too, now walks in the light of God. His funerary procession slowly wove its way though our humble town, and at its head there was not the customary single voice, but one hundred and fifty of his students and followers, all bewigged and with their faces painted white; all playing the great man's works in solemn unison. Never before and never again will there be such a funerary procession, so vivid and musical, so filled with subtlety and profound catharsis. So endeth the voyage of a great man. He will be forever honoured by us all.*

The tragic irony of that last phrase cannot be missed in the light of what was to come only two decades later.

The Hildesheim Trunk

The now famous Hildesheim trunk was discovered in 1983 in the then soon to be demolished ruins of a church in Hildesheim, Germany. Its contents included the hand-written Testament, thought to be by Herr Gratchenfleiss himself, and a book of printed music in an edition dated 1823, with an introduction surprisingly written in English. It is thought they were placed there, inside a casket tomb in the crypt of the church (that of Karl Finkel, who was a student of Herr Gratchenfleiss in the 1790s), to escape the destruction of the Funerary Purges some time in the 1830s. It is most unfortunate that water penetration and the other unsavoury contents of the said tomb had caused the trunk itself to rust heavily and the contents to be largely destroyed by mould. A few fragments of the Testament, together with a handful of the 300 or so pieces in the book, are all that are decipherable.

The music itself is remarkable in many ways: its rigorous abandonment of functional harmony, looking back instead to a more modal style based upon shifting drones, which allows for the occasional use of non-traditional scales; a considerable use of repetition far beyond even the most tedious composers of his day, yet without undermining the notion of a musical journey; the occasional burst of extraordinary dissonance unseen in any other composer since the Renaissance, until the late works of Beethoven fifteen years after Gratchenfleiss's death; the brevity of many of the works (making them momentary glimpses of an emotional state), which predates the later similar smaller works of Schumann by two decades; and his remarkably modern conception of violin technique, treating it more as a rhythm and harmony instrument than a lyrical and melodic single voice. All of these idiosyncrasies are born of the music's unique function – that of the Funerary Violinist: to express the inexpressible; to become the voice of the unnameable sorrows of mourning, and to transfigure them into a vision of hope; to cleanse the soul of the taint of mortal flesh and morbidity.

We will never know whether these were the best or the worst of Gratchenfleiss's many works, nor which pieces were composed when in his long career. Those that have survived are certainly flawed, and it is well known, from the accounts that we have, that he would improvise extravagantly around the written notes, suggesting that these works are really little more than sketches of spaces that he would explore more rigorously in live performance: but they do clearly demonstrate a truly original imagination and a surprisingly modern sensibility. Some of them are remarkably dissonant for his day, and the influence he had on Paganini's Caprices, amongst many other works, is palpable. His abandonment of functional harmony in favour of a rooted drone, in his own words 'to fix the portal in a specific space, and free the music of vain artistry', is a development not seen again until the end of the twentieth century. In addition, the narrative thematic structuring of the works is reminiscent of the much later piano work by Messiaen, *Vingt Regards sur l'Enfant Jesu.*

It is clear from Gratchenfleiss's Testament that he abhorred empty virtuosity, and many of these works could technically be played by the average student, but from accounts of his performances it can be assumed that his own playing was truly exceptional. We can but speculate on the extraordinary wealth of compositional imagination that the book may have once contained, but what can already be stated, unequivocally, is that Herr Gratchenfleiss was a composer and performer of considerable imagination and substance, great renown and tremendous influence, and that even these few works justify a major reassessment of the development of

Thefe pieces are offered, not fo much as a fet, but as a felection of pieces that may be deemed appropriate for the Funerary Violinift. They fhould be performed with great ftoicifm and confiderable regard for both the fanctity of the fpace and the fenfitiuity of the affembled company. I haue not put in many dynamics, nor fpeed indications, as thefe fhould be dictated by the Spirit of the moment. If you are not liftening to that fpirit then you are failing in intent and therefore execution.

For the Funerary Artift there is no room for pretenfion or artifice; the funerary ritual cannot countenance the cafual glorification of perfona, which as is fo common amongft the generality of muficians today. Only that which befits the procliuities of earneft funerary activity may be countenanced.

A Funerary Violinift is NOT a performer of mufic - he is part fpiritual medium, part prieft, and moft of all, the very channel through which the diftreffed find folace, the afeared find peace, the weak find ftrength and the humbled find dignity. He is the chalice that holds the wine and the pen that holds the ink. He is the bridge ouer the riuer and the telefcope that fees beyond the ftars. Refpect thy calling and ye fhall find Virtue and Truth; deny thy path and ye fhall Fall!

The curious amateur may be moued to remark vpon the predominance of the key of G minor in this modeft collection, howeuer the worthy ftudent of Funerary Violin will be well aware that G minor is the key moft beloued of all to the Spirit of Death, and hence it is vnauoidable that this fame key fhould be predominant.

Herr Hieronymous Gratchenfleiß, 1809.

---

14. The back page of the printed book found in the Hildesheim trunk, now known as 'The Funerary Notebooks of Herr Gratchenfleiss'. Regrettably both the front page and the title page were too badly damaged by mould to be preserved.

virtuosic violin music, if not the evolution of funerary history itself. Despite attempts to eradicate his legacy, attempts that were only truly undermined by the discovery of the Hildesheim trunk, it is clear that his vision had a considerable influence on later musicians and that, without him, the later masterpieces of Paganini, Schumann and Chopin, to name but a few, could not have been written as they were. It could even be said that the Hildesheim trunk is the most important discovery in the history of music since Mendelssohn and Schumann visited Schubert's brother in 1829 to uncover a cupboardful of unperformed works, which now form the very backbone of musical Romanticism.

Wolfgang Amadeus Mozart

Not a Funerary Violinist?

Though Mozart is obviously more renowned for his work as a composer and pianist, in 1787 his musical career was to take an oblique turn as a result of direct contact with the Austrian court. He had never had much luck with court appointments. Emperor Joseph II had given him a (mostly honorary) position as Imperial Royal Chamber Composer – a post presented to him, according to Count Von Chotek (financial director at court) in a letter dated March 1792, 'simply in view of the fact that such a rare genius in the field of music should not have to seek his bread and butter in foreign countries'. The post provided very little income, and few commissions, but amongst Mozart's responsibilities were the composition of dance music for the Imperial balls, and Funerary Violin music for 'persons of note'. One such person was Johann Gottfried Albrecht, a banker and minor politician, whose death in May 1791 would have been completely forgotten if it weren't for two interesting documents that have recently come to light. The first is an entry in the diary of Count Carl Zinzendorf for 21 May:

Attended Albrecht's funeral today. Having heard rumours that Mozart would perform on the viola the crowd was considerable and there was much muttering. Finally, after what seemed like a most tedious hour, the coffin was processed down the aisle to what must be the most beautiful funerary dirge that ever sprang from a viola. Mozart is truly a genius. The whole of us were awed. Then followed the most tedious of sermons before, once again, Mozart put bow to string and it seemed that the very angels were in tears. It was a fitting tribute to a memorably punctual man. Then on to the Court ball. The confusion bored me. The Queen of Naples greeted me graciously. The Empress gambled, and later, showed her ankles. [translated from the original German]

The second document is a receipt in Mozart's own hand for the payment of 10 ducats (45 florins) for the composition of three funerary sonatas for solo viola, and the performance thereof on 1 May, 16 May and 21 May, on which Mozart signed:

too much for what I did, too little for what I could do. W. A. Mozart.

This receipt shows that Mozart had performed at three funerals that month, and we can only assume that this was a regular occurrence. It is a tragedy that we cannot know what these pieces were, as no solo violin or viola works survive. We can only assume that the manuscripts were either destroyed in the Great Funerary Purges of the 1830s and 1840s, or that maybe they will be found one day in the secret library of the Vatican.

Pierre Dubuisson

Grand Master of the Funerary Duel

15. This flattering miniature portrait, painted in 1805 by an unknown artist, shows Dubuisson at the age of twenty, as he wanted to be seen.

Of all the important figures to influence the evolution of the Art of Funerary Violin during its final flourish in the early nineteenth century, Pierre Dubuisson remains possibly the most enigmatic, because of the extraordinary lack of official records that have survived. Specifically targeted by the Great Funerary Purges during the 1830s, he is indeed thought by many scholars to have disappeared in 1838 as the result of a direct order from the Vatican itself; it is likely that very few records of his life and work survived even into the latter half of that century, and the two world wars that followed, during which a great many historical and governmental documents were destroyed, have further compounded the problem. For a long time virtually all that was known of him was the tantalising accounts left in the writings of Charles Sudbury (see the next chapter), in which there is a vivid portrayal of one of his performances, and a number of references to conversations between the two of them. It was not until 1990, when a collection of wax cylinders recorded by Ferdinand Brunot in 1913 were rediscovered, together with transcripts of a substantial interview between Brunot and Jacques Dubuisson, Pierre Dubuisson's grandson, that a fuller picture began to emerge.

Although, of course, family mythologies are rarely reliable enough to be taken at face value, in this case there is small choice, as without his grandson's comments and reminiscences we would know very little indeed about a man whose few surviving works show him to have been one of the greatest artists to work within the medium. The following outline of his life should therefore be considered a compilation of hearsay and conjecture, coloured in with the occasional fact, and it is therefore entirely possible that many elements could be considerably revised with the discovery of further documents at any time in the future.

Thought to have been born in 1785, on the outskirts of Paris near the Bois de Vincennes, Pierre Dubuisson rose to become France's foremost Funerary Violinist of the early nineteenth century. In 1801, aged sixteen, he won a place at the Conservatoire National de Musique et de Déclamation (later to become the Paris Conservatoire) to study with Rudolph Kreutzer, although, according to his grand-

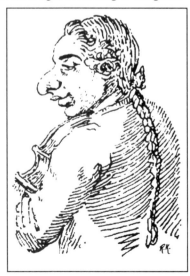

16. This sketch by Richard Kraven, penned during Dubuisson's 1823 visit to England, is rather less flattering than the earlier miniature. Admittedly a caricature, it does nonetheless suggest that Dubuisson had an unusually large nose. Which of the two images is more accurate is not known as they are the only representations of him to have survived; however, it is possible that his nose had grown considerably during the intervening eighteen years as a result of either the abuse of alcohol or an unfortunate cyst.

son, he fell out with his tutor in 1805 as a result of his interest in Funerary Violin, and was expelled. The following year he apprenticed himself to Jean-Paul Lambert, Funerary Violinist for the 'village' of Montmartre, and it is believed that he continued working as Lambert's assistant until 1810, when he accepted his own post in the district of St Germain.

It was in 1815 that he made his name in the 'funerary duels' that had become a great, if temporary, fashion all over France. The origins of this sudden fashion were until recently entirely obscure, but a document that came to light early in 2000 suggests a very specific situation as the initial catalyst for a bizarre scene that went on to catch the imagination of all Paris.

On 22 July 1812, Vincent Lefèbvre, an officer in Napoleon's army fighting under Marshal Marmont in the Peninsular War, was killed during the Battle of Salamanca. He had been a notable patron of the arts and an amateur composer, who counted amongst his close friends a number of Funerary Violinists, including Benoît Hachée and Christophe Harquin, who, it seems, were arch-rivals. Being an officer of some note, Lebèbvre's body was brought back to France for burial in the cemetery of Père-Lachaise on 20 August, and a dispute soon arose over who would take up the violin for the funeral. Both Hachée and Harquin petitioned the family to be chosen, and after many arguments and counter-arguments it was agreed that they would both perform, taking turns at improvising upon one of the more plaintive melodies by Lefèbvre himself. Honoré Givry, who was present at the funeral and knew both participants, takes up the story in a letter to Henri Bédard, who, it is assumed from the tone of the letter, also knew both protagonists personally:

> *The proceedings soon became something of a spectacle with both Benoît and Christophe desperately trying to upstage each other in a manner not at all befitting the circumstances. The chosen melody (I can't recall what it was from) was passed back and forth, each time becoming slower and more sonorous, until all trace of it was lost in what was, by then, little more than a demonstration of tragic dissonance and resolution, although it must be admitted that the music was profoundly moving. Never has the heart been so worn upon the sleeve as then, and by the end I was not certain whether those assembled would laugh, cry, or burst into applause. As it was they simply stood in silence absorbing the moment as Christophe and Benoît slowly bowed and left the graveside. It was not until the following evening that I realised all of Paris was talking of this most bizarre of funerary performances ...* [translated from the original French]

What had been born of petty rivalry soon became a fashion that spread all about France amongst the wealthy and noteworthy. The soon to be deceased would leave a fragment of melody with his will, and two Funerary Violinists would improvise in turn upon the theme at the funeral, each attempting to draw more tragedy from it than his opponent: the winner being the artist who drew the most tears from the assembled crowd. (For a detailed description of just such a performance by Pierre Dubuisson and Jean-Paul Couret, see the chapter on Charles Sudbury.)

Again, according to his grandson Jacques, it was as a result of Dubuisson's undoubted popular successes in the funerary duels of 1815 that he was appointed Surintendant des Violonistes Funèbres du Roi to Louis XVIII in 1816, though he continued to perform in the duels of Père-Lachaise until 1821, when the fashion began to wane. Unfortunately, all records regarding the post of Surintendant des Violonistes Funèbres du Roi for the period from 1790 until its dissolution in 1830 were lost, probably during the German occupation of the Second World War, and so it is impossible to verify the specifics of this claim. However, there is a brief mention of Dubuisson in this role amongst the papers of Charles Sudbury, in a letter dated 10 May 1824 (never sent), and so it can be assumed that Dubuisson did indeed hold the position at some point during the 1820s. For the precise dates of his tenure we will, for now, have to take Jacques's word.

Dubuisson's association with the Royal Court resulted in his spending four months in hiding during Napoleon's Hundred Days, and it was at this time that he began to develop his ideas for a unified Funerary Suite. After Waterloo, he returned to his post with a new vision of the Funerary Suite, consolidating many of the striking, though untidy, ideas of Herr Gratchenfleiss into a neat seven-movement work. In 1827 he was elected president of the newly formed French branch of the Guild of Funerary Violinists, and under his leadership the Guild, and its performers, gradually took on something of a cult status around France, integrating Funerary Violin into the general Catholic funeral ritual and attributing great religious significance to all aspects of the funerary performance. He continued his official position under Charles X, until his forced resignation (under pressure from the Vatican) in 1830.

It is clear from a number of comments in Charles Sudbury's *Considerations of the Funerary Arts* that during the 1830s Dubuisson was particularly vocal in defending the Art during the Great Funerary Purges, speaking out against persecution and repression by the Catholic Church, and performing publicly at many funerals of the noteworthy, despite the danger. In 1838 he disappeared from his rooms in dubious circumstances, leaving a note, later proved not to be in his hand, which stated that he had left to take up holy orders in Valencia. All his papers and scores had gone, but none of his clothes, which aroused considerable suspicion and rumour at the time. Today it is assumed that he was one of many victims of the Vatican's agents during the Great Funerary Purges.

The *Sept Regards sur l'Esprit de la Mort* of 1826 is a typical example of the Funerary Suite of the period, as developed by Dubuisson and Sudbury, with the requisite seven movements: three Marches, a Panic, a Flight, a Eulogy and a Dream (not in any prescribed order). At present only one hand-written copy of the score has been uncovered (found amongst Sudbury's few papers that survived the fire at the Guild's offices in 1841), together with a recording made by Jacques Dubuisson in 1913, which occasionally differs slightly from the written score (this can probably be put down to a confusion of Jacques's memory, and the score printed in this book follows the notes as written, not as recorded). The music itself is also quite typical, being fundamentally modal, using unusual time signatures and changes, and having a greater degree of dissonance than was common in other musical forms of the period. The influence of Herr Gratchenfleiss is clearly audible, though it has been contained and sensualised in the expected French manner.

The movements are all monothematic, and contain a single emotional space in the manner of the Baroque (despite its fundamentally Romantic vision, Funerary Violin never embraced the emotional transitions of classical and Romantic music, believing that the time for emotional development is over at death, and should be replaced with spiritual focus). One element that is characteristic of Dubuisson's music is the use of major/minor changes within phrases, and these can be heard most clearly in the first, third and last movements. Although such alternations are known in the works of Herr Gratchenfleiss, it was Dubuisson who saw the huge potential they offered and developed them into the basis for entire themes. The fourth movement, although harmonic, is barely tonal and sets a precedent for the lyrical chromaticism and harmonic abandonment of Debussy. In addition, the whole conception of the suite, being a series of views or images of the Spirit of Death, anticipates Olivier Messiaen's *Vingt Regards sur l'Enfant Jesu* by over a hundred years.

* * * * *

Famous posthumously, and exclusively as a result of the handful of recordings he made, Jacques Dubuisson was, as already stated, the grandson of Pierre Dubuisson. Born in 1862, he never met his illustrious ancestor, who had died some fourteen years earlier, but grew up in an environment much dominated by 'Grand Pierre'. When interviewed in later life, he described a miserable childhood, tyrannised by his father, Michel Dubuisson, a failed musician and drunk who forced him into endless hours of practising the family legacy. Though displaying some talent, he soon learned to hate the violin, his father, and the works of Pierre, which had formed the basis of his practice regime, and at the age of sixteen he ran away from his family home in Bordeaux to seek adventure on the streets of Paris. After a period of seven years, which he would never speak of, he finally got a regular job as a schoolteacher at l'Ecole Saint-Germain de Charonne, a post that he held until 1927. He continued to play the violin, as an amateur, giving occasional concerts including those works by his grandfather that had been his albatross as a child. Though only an average amateur violinist, he gave concerts throughout the years 1892 to1922, finding that his repertoire of funerary works by his grandfather gave him a unique selling point, and proved to be fairly popular.

It was at just such a concert in 1913, at the Èglise Saint-Julien-le-Pauvre, that Ferdinand Brunot, a sound archivist from the Bibliothèque Nationale de France, came upon him, and seeing his music not as French concert music but as an interesting ethnographic novelty, persuaded Jacques Dubuisson to make a recording of a typical example of one of his grandfather's Funerary Suites. These recordings were made on $4\frac{1}{2}$-minute wax cylinders, and have remained in the archives of the Bibliothèque Nationale de France ever since, together with the transcript of the interview already mentioned.

It is impossible to know how much the playing carries the influence of Pierre Dubuisson. Certainly Pierre would have taught Michel, and Michel in turn would have taught Jacques, but years of failure and alcohol abuse must have taken their toll on Michel, and Jacques is certainly not the brilliant virtuoso that his grandfather must have been, given his reputation. However, though Jacques's playing has many technical deficiencies, there is no doubt that he plays with spirit and clearly understands the intention behind the music.

Jacques Dubuisson died at his home, south of Paris, on the 16 November 1937 and was buried in the Thiais cemetery, on 20 November. No violinist was present, nor was any music played.

*17. & 18. The above photographs are from the funeral of Jacques
Dubuisson, 1937, and were kindly donated by the family.*

Charles Sudbury

England's Dark Genius of Funerary Violin

19. Charles Sudbury in 1810

Charles Henry Sudbury was born on 22 April 1790 in the small village of Groton, Suffolk, and though his name was recorded in the parish register of St Bartholomew's Church, he was brought up as a Catholic. His father, Henry Charles Sudbury, was a scholar at Cambridge, a writer of school textbooks, and a Catholic lay preacher, whose commitment to his faith, and its revival in England, was demonstrated by his joining the Cisalpine Club upon its foundation in 1792. However, despite this well-constructed veneer of respectability, he had a reputation for drunkenness and violence, and frequently found himself in court on charges ranging from public debauch (1788, 1789, 1793, 1796, 1803, 1810), drunkenness (1788, 1792, 1797, 1805, 1807) and assault (1793, 1795, 1802) to tax evasion (1799, 1806), each time getting away with a fine. The charges of bigamy that were levelled in 1802 were later withdrawn.

Charles was the youngest of four boys and two girls, and his mother, Elizabeth Mary, had died shortly after his birth. Little is known of his early years (it can be assumed he was initially educated by his father), but in 1798, at the age of eight, he was sent to attend a preparatory school in London, and moved from there to Christ's Hospital in 1802 as a 'blue coat' charity scholar. Whilst there he became a noted student of the classics, theology, Platonic philosophy and music, and dabbled in many radical authors of the time. It was also there that he took up the violin, displaying 'considerably greater than the normal aptitude', as noted by Adolphus Wilton, the visiting music instructor at the Hospital, and later co-founder of the ill-fated Hampstead School of Poetry and Music. Sudbury was by all accounts a popular boy, excellent in debate, and a fine sportsman, though years later, in 1852, Thomas Adderley, a former classmate, was to recall how 'a skulking sense of doom and foreboding seemed to follow him around like a familiar'.

During the holidays he would rarely return to Groton, preferring to stay with an aunt in London, Gladys Elberton, a widow who had married well and widowed better. She had a large house in Chelsea, with a Bohemian reputation, and frequently held artistic soirées: it was at these soirées, over the next twenty years, until his aunt's death in 1826, that Sudbury was to meet the thinkers, writers, poets and musicians of the day, including William Godwin, Leigh Hunt, Shelley, Coleridge, Byron, and many others, opening his eyes to the growing, as yet unnamed, Romantic movement.

In 1808, at the age of eighteen, Sudbury went up to Jesus College, Cambridge, on a Christ's Hospital Exhibition, with a generous allowance from his aunt. Although he excelled himself intellectually, the 'skulking sense of doom' was still plaguing him, and was increasingly noted by his fellow students. A recently discovered letter, dated 22 October 1810, from fellow undergraduate Peter Ostrey (who graduated in law in 1812) to his cousin Michael Ostrey, is typical of contemporary descriptions:

> *I am increasingly concerned about Charles, whose behaviour is becoming deeply erratic. He was always given to wild passions, and moments of excess,*

but of late these have taken on a darker hue. He studies Theology and Philosophy with the zeal of a martyr, and was recently reprimanded by Sir Harold for distributing a leaflet entitled 'The Catholic Church is the Worship of the Antichrist' – a detestable document full of violent rhetoric and vehement intolerance. He seems determined to set himself against the general way of things, and whilst we speak of Freedom and Justice, and (in secret meetings) Atheism, he rails at the Catholics, depicting them as the very servants of the Devil. He has grown his hair long, and is drinking considerably. There are also rumours that he has a boy in the village, and certainly he spends much time there. It is a tragedy to see so fine and complex a mind tear itself apart for no discernable reason. I regret to say that if things continue in this way I will no longer be able to count him a friend …

In an as yet unpublished journal by another fellow undergraduate, Jonas Maynard (who was to become a Baptist minister in Northumberland, 1823–52), dated 16 February 1811, we have a more personal account:

Sudbury scares me. There is something cold and evil in his eyes, like the look of a man who has walked with Death and now, no longer sees the beauty of life for fear of that secret which he alone knows. He locks himself in his room for days at a time, shouting incomprehensibly to himself, or whatever figment of his wild imagination he has conjured, or playing darkly sombre music on his violin, which he only seems to play alone, and when he emerges I can feel his dark presence looming all along the corridor. Woe betide any who get in his way, for at them he hisses like a Devil and offers up the Evil Eye. Were it not for his constant preaching of God's word, I would be convinced he had made his pact with Lucifer, and was conducting secret rituals behind that door …

The above descriptions paint an extreme picture of the young Sudbury, but history and scholarship have explained at least some of this behaviour. The 'village' referred to is in fact the town of Cambridge, and the 'boy' was Evelyn Hopkinson, the fifteen-year-old son of the Cambridge Funerary Violinist George Hopkinson. Sudbury had secretly apprenticed himself to Hopkinson in 1809, and developed an intense relationship with his son, Evelyn, whom Sudbury referred to as 'my little Puck'. The 'darkly sombre music' he played was almost certainly the Funerary Notebooks of Herr Gratchenfleiss, which we know, from his own writings, were his introduction to the art. We also know, from the records kept by Cambridge apothecary H. R. Reynolds, that Sudbury had started taking laudanum for 'intense headaches' in 1809, which could account for some of his less rational behaviour. Why he became obsessed with disavowing the Catholic Church is less clear, but it may well have something to do with the Catholic hypocrisies he saw first hand in the behaviour of his father. He was always deeply religious, though his world philosophy was, in time, to challenge many aspects of Christian belief and, ultimately, to contribute to the savage vengeance of the Vatican in the Great Funerary Purges of the 1830s and 1840s.

In 1811 he was sent down from Cambridge for 'behaviour not befitting a gentleman', and many unsubstantiated rumours abounded, from sodomy to devil worship, though none was ever proven. For a time he was socially disgraced, but the 1810s were a period of many radical ideas, and this disgrace only added to his prestige amongst the thinkers and writers of his aunt's literary set, making of him a minor celebrity. He moved back to his aunt's house in Chelsea with Puck, and for a few months they lived very happily together until a row of unsurpassed violence and insobriety, after which their friendship never wholly recovered and Puck returned to Cambridge. With a recommendation from Hopkinson, Sudbury continued his apprenticeship in Funerary Violin under Joseph Burkham, the then secretary of the Guild of Funerary Violinists, a Freemason and member of the Antients Grand Lodge of London. Burkham was, by all accounts a learned man, a free-thinker and a pantheist, who was elected secretary on the basis of his 'profound moderation in all things'. It can be assumed that he had a calming influence on the young Sudbury, now twenty-one, as accounts of his eccentricity and vehemence are much more understated for a time.

In 1813 Sudbury completed his apprenticeship, was made a junior member of the Guild of Funerary Violinists, and received his first official appointment: that of 2nd Funerary Violinist to the parish of Lambeth, a post he held for four years until July 1817, playing for many of the poorer funerals, for a fee of two half-crowns. Parish records indicate that he performed at an average of two funerals a week, totalling 453 over the entire period, although since none of the deceased were persons of note, no other accounts of his parish work have, as yet, been uncovered.

However, we know of one other notable event during this period. In 1813, after nearly seventy years of feuding and disavowals, the two rival factions of Freemasonry in England, the Antients and the Moderns, decided to lay down their differences and join forces: the twenty-one Articles of Union were drawn up and the Grand Lodge of England was born. This union brought intellectuals of many different philosophic persuasions to the debating table, and also gave freemasonry a greater confidence after many years of Catholic persecution (something we will hear more of later), leading many lodges to open their door to new members. In February 1814 Sudbury was admitted to the Grand Lodge of London, under the invitation of Burkham, where he was to meet many influential politicians, artists and patrons of late Hanoverian England, including William Beckford, Member of Parliament for Hindon, writer, collector, musician and extravagant eccentric, who was to become Sudbury's most important patron for the rest of his life.

William Beckford was, by all accounts, an unusual man. Son of William Beckford, the London merchant and friend of Pitt, he inherited a huge fortune, which even his lifelong extravagances could not squander, in part due to the many West Indian plantations that he owned but took no interest in. He was educated privately as his mother distrusted academic institutions, and did not attend university, but his essays, satires and poems demonstrate he was a far-sighted man, of considerable intellect and untamed passions. He was also a fine amateur musician and counted Mozart amongst his childhood music teachers.

20. The west end of William Beckford's 'ruined abbey' in Fonthill Gifford, here depicted in 1850, after the tower had collapsed. Despite its ruined appearance, it did in fact have a great many luxuriously habitable rooms.

Thirteen years older than Sudbury, he took an immediate paternal interest in the passionate young man, and frequently invited him to stay at his estate in Fonthill Gifford, Wiltshire, where he had built a ruined abbey, with some habitable rooms, a 276-foot tower, and a massive ballroom with 120-foot ceilings – one of the most renowned follies in England at the time. In his *Considerations of the Funerary Arts* (1838) (a cross between a memoir, a manifesto and an instruction manual – which sadly is now lost, with the exception of fifty or so pages salvaged from the great fire at the Guild offices in 1841), Sudbury refers to the many happy hours he spent with Beckford, sat beside the 20-foot fireplace in the ballroom, discussing natural philosophy, theology and music, or playing the violin in 'that monstrously fine acoustic'.

21. James Rumsay, known as 'Brandy', painted in 1823. This picture, a miniature on ivory, was commissioned by Sudbury as a birthday present for Brandy, and originally came with a matching portrait of Sudbury himself. When Brandy died in 1826, Sudbury placed his own portrait in Brandy's coffin, and thereafter kept this picture with him at all times. It was found in his waistcoat pocket after his own death, in the fire of 1841, remarkably undamaged.

In August 1817, having left his parish post on the promise of an annuity from Beckford (which amounted to £250 per year and was paid until 1839), Sudbury embarked on a tour of Europe with James Rumsay, fourth son of Earl Rumsay, a gentleman and profligate whom he had met at the Grand Lodge. James, who was known as 'Brandy' to his friends (possibly because of his often excessive drinking habits), was twenty-two, of a weak constitution and unquenchable appetites, and prone to seizures. His doctors had recommended continental air and regular bleeding, and the two young men, who had not known each other well up to this time, decided to travel together.

The tour, originally planned to last a year, was cut short to six months in part as a result of outbreaks of yellow fever and cholera in many parts of Italy, and in part because of Brandy's own poor health. They spent four months in Italy, two of them studying antiquities in Rome, and then a further two months returning via Tuscany, Piedmont and France. During this trip Sudbury witnessed two violin performances that had a profound influence upon him, performances he was moved to recall twenty years later in his *Considerations of the Funerary Arts.*

The first, in December 1818 in Milan, was a public concert by the now legendary Paganini, who was, at the time, unknown outside Italy. In his *Considerations* of 1838, Sudbury was to recall:

It was a concert unlike any I had ever seen. He played entirely solo, as we do, but for the living, and in a manner fervently devoid of the spiritual dimension, as if he had no conception of the visionary power of a solo violin. Never did he let the instrument speak in its natural voice, without mimicking some absurd accent or folly. Never did he let a simple melody breath without exploding in a burst of nonsensical and frivolous ornamentation. And all the while the crowds were cheering with all the discrimination of a flock of starlings. I felt it to be a tragedy that God could waste such technical mastery on one who clearly had no gift for music. And a far greater tragedy still, that the culture that gave us civilisation itself should now be reduced to mistaking a clown for a prophet! I vowed, in that moment, to dedicate myself to utter mastery of my own art, and through that art, to show the world what profound revelations can be drawn from the strings of a solo violin ...

(As is shown in the Guild's publication *The Great Funerary Purges,* Paganini, or rather his success and infamy, was to play a not inconsequential role in the instigation of the Funerary Purges twelve years later.)

The other violin performance that was to have an influence upon Sudbury was not a concert but a funerary recital, or rather a duel, between Pierre Dubuisson and Jean-Paul Couret, for the interment of Georges Couthon, a notable Parisian wine merchant, at the cemetery of Père-Lachaise. In the years following the Revolution, a unique and short-lived fashion for funerary duels between two violinists had grown up in France: the soon to be deceased would leave a fragment of melody with his will, and two Funerary Violinists would improvise in turn upon the theme at the interment, each attempting to conjure more tragedy from it than his opponent – the winner being the artist who drew the most tears from the assembled crowd. Although initially disgusted by the notion of competitive funerary performances, Sudbury found the imagination and sincerity of the players, particularly Dubuisson, most compelling, as he reveals in his *Considerations:*

Imagine my surprise at seeing the Duel advertised on billboards all over Paris, together with bold caricatures of the players, and an offer of wine, bread and cheese. Poor Couthon seemed hardly remembered in the spectacle of his own funeral ... We assembled in the mid afternoon, once the service itself was concluded, and gathered at the graveside. Many rows of chairs were laid out for the spectators, and, behind them, there was a long table serving refreshments as promised, including bread, cheese and snails in garlic butter, together with a choice of fine regional wines. Immediately the performers arrived the hubbub turned to a murmur, and then to an expectant silence. Ladies stood fanning themselves affectedly, and gentlemen removed their hats. After a brief moment spent tuning their violins they took their positions, with Dubuisson at the head of the grave, and Couret at the foot. With deep solemnity, worthy of a Funerary Violinist, they intoned the sombre melody in perfect unison, then paused, bowed formally to each other, and the duel began.

Couret, who it turned out was the challenger, took the first variation, playing through the melody with the simplest of subtle ornaments, and pouring forth pathos and maudlin earnestness with an ever-widening vibrato that would have seemed uncouth in any other context. Slowing considerably towards the close of this, his first statement, he dwelt upon the cadence with a particularly fierce frown, and, upon arriving at its close, concluded with a florid bow to the audience that seemed more than a little out of place, but drew much applause nonetheless.

Throughout this time Dubuisson had stood, stock still as cemetery furniture, emanating the quiet dignity one would expect from an acknowledged master, in the face of a childish challenge. Finally, once the applause had died away, he raised his bow to the violin and opened with a single preparatory note so deeply wreathed in sombre woe that it would have melted the heart of even the coolest of politicians or executioners. Then, ever so slowly, he solemnly intoned the notes of the tune, dry as the bones beneath his feet, in the perfect conjuration of the hollow barrenness of mortality, making us all feel aghast at the emptiness of our own lives; before introducing, with the subtlety of a wily cleric, the smallest glimpse of hope amidst tragedy and peace amidst despair, through the clever and most emotional use of the upside down mordant. Finally, before closing this, his first statement, he took the simple melody and somehow, as if in a dream, turned it on its head, revealing how the soul will rise and, just for a moment, we glimpsed the very gates of heaven itself. As he lifted his bow from the strings there was a shocked and utter silence from the assembled crowd, and it must have been nearly a minute before we could shake ourselves from the heavenly images he had so presented, and erupt into rapturous cheers and applause. At this point I felt great pity for poor Couret, the poor pretender, who was so obviously out of his league, and yet duty bound to continue ...

This description continues, in similar vein, for many pages, detailing the general tone and techniques applied by the performers, in often poetical and melodramatic terms. Finally, after four more statements from each of the players, Sudbury describes the conclusion of the duel:

And as he [Dubuisson] drew to a close, slowly leading us down into the very deepest depths of unremitting misery, I was momentarily distracted by the gentle sound of sobbing from an elegantly dressed young lady to my right, and, removed from the profound reverie he had so masterfully induced, I looked around and saw that each and every feminine countenance present was streaked with quiet tears, and every gentleman, his head bowed in an exaggeration of despair, was locked in the most profoundly tragic and mournful of contemplations. It was immediately clear that the duel was over, and as Dubuisson lifted his bow from the string for the final time, Couret, a pale and exhausted imitation of his former self, merely bowed to his opponent and vanquisher, and then turned his back upon us, walking off brusquely between the many tombs, not even taking the time to replace his violin in its box (this was attended to by his servant who followed behind him like a nervous puppy). Dubuisson then acknowledged his victory with a noble nod of his head, packed up his own violin, and then purposefully strode away, with an air of might and dignity I have only ever seen before in an English Lord.

This entirely abhorrent and misjudged spectacle, which served no obvious spiritual nor memorial purpose, would have been no better than any music hall entertainment were it not for the unquestionable genius of Dubuisson himself, who held within his heart and hands the power to speak directly to both the Spirit and to God himself. Never have I heard such true notes played, such profound communication with both the dead and the living, entirely free from the dual sins of egoism and vanity so often present in the funerary arts. At that moment I knew that the future would bring us together

*both as colleagues and friends, and that, in some way, we were fated to lift
the art of Funerary Violin out of its stagnant and corrupted tarn of vice, and
raise it up to the true and sacred heights to which it once so naturally
ascended ...*

Quite what he meant by 'its stagnant and corrupted tarn of vice' is uncertain,
although it is clear that Sudbury enjoyed a melodramatic style of writing, and it
may be no more than an affectation to emphasise the heights of which he dreamed.
(There is no evidence of corruption amongst Funerary Violinists of this period, and
the Chiswick scandals of the 1790s, in which additional obligatory costs were
added to the Violinist's fee for the hire of a violin, bow and black ribbons, had been
firmly dealt with by the Guild at the time.) The impression Dubuisson made on him
was to be borne out by a sudden change in his own pieces, which expanded their
vision, for the first time, beyond simple marches and the works of Herr Gratchenfleiss, to include a whole vision of a sacred rite. Four years later, when Dubuisson
travelled to England, they were to work together in formalising the Funerary Suite
to free it from 'the ever-present potential for indulgence and moral decay'.

22. This plaque was erected in Cadogan
Square in 1982 as a result of
considerable anonymous representations
by the Guild to the Greater London
Council.

Shortly after Sudbury's return to England in February 1818, William Entwistle,
President of the Guild of Funerary Violinists, died of syphilitic complications at
the age of forty-seven. After a number of notoriously heated debates, Joseph
Beckham was elected President and offered Sudbury the post of Secretary, at £80
per annum, which he accepted graciously. Now, at the age of twenty-eight, with a
substantial annuity and a position in the establishment, Sudbury had made himself
a true London gentleman. He rented a suite of furnished rooms in Cadogan Square,
two doors down from the Rumsay family town house, and by all accounts spent
much of his time in the company of Brandy. Although there were many unsubstantiated and frequently unspoken rumours about the nature of their relationship, there
is no evidence to suggest that their friendship was anything other than that which
was normal amongst bachelors of the time. In his role as Secretary to the Guild, he

was regularly called upon to perform at the funerals of 'persons of some, but not considerable, note', and these included Sir Samuel Romilly (1818), Sir William Cornwallis (1819), Richmal Mangnall (1820), Benjamin West (1820), Arthur Young (1820), Arthur Thistlewood – a mock funeral without the body, which had been given over for dissection as he died on the gallows for high treason – (1820), John Crome (1821), David Ricardo (1823), Edward Jenner (1823), Reginald Heber (1826), John Cartwright (1824), Samuel Crompton (1827), George Canning (1827), Richard Parkes Bonington (1828), Thomas Bewick (1828), Sir Humphry Davy (1829), and many others besides. The student of late Hanoverian English history will note what a veritable who's who of politicians, thinkers and writers this is: a testament not only to the high regard in which Sudbury was held at this time, but also to the prevalence of Freemasonry amongst the London elite, for it was through his connection with the Great Lodge that many of these invitations arose.

It was at the funeral of Sir William Cornwallis on 6 June 1819 that Sudbury first came to the attention of the then Prince Regent. Contrary to the current popular image of George IV as a hugely overweight, self-indulgent womaniser devoted to decadence and debauch of all kinds, somewhere inside his enormous frame was a more fastidious character, a fine connoisseur of the arts, collector, builder of richly decorated palaces and one of England's greatest artistic patrons – for example, it was he who persuaded the government to purchase the Angerstein collection in 1824 (for £57,000), which became the nucleus of the National Gallery. He took a great interest in music, often inviting leading performers to his Pavilion in Brighton to give private recitals to the congregation of wealthy social misfits he gathered around him, in his specially designed oriental music room. Sudbury's first command performance was in March 1820, and over the next ten years he was to perform for the king on seventeen occasions: a duty he deeply resented, as stated in his *Considerations*, on the following grounds:

> *It is well known that I have always played for the dead, and them alone, and yet this Fatuous Flatulent Oaf repeatedly commanded that I perform for his and his entourage's entertainment, as if they were themselves already cold in the ground with worms crawling through them: Oh! If only! And I would have been freed from this monstrous distortion and desecration of my Sacred Art ...*

Despite Sudbury's reservations, this association with the king did inevitably raise his profile and, though he refused outright to perform for any other potential patrons (barring, of course, the occasional informal demonstration amongst his close friends), he found himself to be increasingly popular with the higher social classes, and his performance at a funeral could be guaranteed to at least triple the public attendance, making him much sought after.

As already mentioned, the visit of Pierre Dubuisson to England in April 1823 was to have a profound effect on the evolution of the Funerary Suite, for both Dubuisson and Sudbury. Initially, Dubuisson was sent by the family of Alain Sublette, who had died unexpectedly whilst conducting business in London, to perform at his interment in the French manner, but his meeting with Sudbury, at a ceremony of the Grand Lodge (Dubuisson was also a Freemason and member of the Grand Orient of France), resulted in a stay of six weeks. On 26 April, a week after the said interment, the two retreated to the Beckford Estate in Fonthill Gifford, where they spent a month together with their host, William Beckford, discussing music, poetry, love, spirits and the Funerary Arts. During this time they laid down the foundations of what was to become the Funerary Suite: a seven-movement work that should contain three Marches (in the broadest sense), a Panic, a Dream, a Eulogy and a Flight. In his *Considerations of the Funerary Arts,* a series of essays and memoirs written throughout the 1830s, Sudbury describes the aesthetic requirements for such a suite in some, but not considerable, detail.

In 1826, just as everything was going exceptionally well for Sudbury, tragedy struck. Brandy died on 12 November of 'a fever of the brain, brought on by excessive imbibance over a sustained period'. Despite his professional experience in dealing with the mortality of those unconnected to him personally, this particular death seemed to break something within him, from which he never fully recovered. For a full six months he retreated to his rooms, dressing, according to the accounts of Dr Theodore Sanders, 'in nothing but a long black silk dressing gown, smoking heavily upon his pipe, and drinking rather more than is advisable in a man of his condition'. Dr Sanders' records also indicate that he had started taking laudanum again, in not insubstantial quantities.

During this period of deep mourning he wrote a set of twenty-four poems, which he entitled *In Memoriam,* and which were published at his own expense, under the name of Frances Feaver White, in June 1824, to considerable critical acclaim and some social outrage. Samuel Taylor Coleridge, for example, wrote to his friend and fellow poet Robert Southey:

I have this morning been reading a strange publication – viz. Poems with
very wild and passionate emphasis upon the two fundamental conditions of

man – Love and Mortality – In Memoriam, by Frances Feaver White. Mr White is in many ways almost a Genius, – and, I apprehend, a Swedenborgian certainly – a Mystic possibly. He has painted Death with all the grace and insight of an Old Friend: verily I am the very mire of common-sense compared with Mr White …

Most of the verses refer to love, death and music, and though by no means great writing, they offer a valuable insight into the formation of Sudbury's Funerary Aesthetic, something he was to write about with considerable zeal throughout the 1830s. The poem 'Where Flew His Soul?' is a typical example:

WHERE FLEW HIS SOUL?

Where flew his soul this wint'ry night
That knew until today the pleasures of the world
And wore his youthful body with unrivalled grace
Before Death's hand, he kissed, and bowed to God?

Where flew the spirit of unbuttoned charm
And beauty unsurpassed; that left its mark
Only in a dead thing; a pretence of calm
Where no light shines, no single spark
Remains: where flesh is doomed to rot to nought
And worms will feast upon his sensuous limbs?

Where flew the part of him with whom I fought
And touched and loved; now subtle as a dream
That echoes evermore upon the wind
His memory as empty as the oft-vibrating air,
And mournful as the tones drawn from my violin?

(Charles Sudbury, 1826)

Despite the rather clumsy last line, this poem touches on many of the ideas that Sudbury was later to hone in his *Considerations of the Funerary Arts*. The style and structural freedom demonstrate that he was well aware of the new Romantic poets, such as Byron and Shelley (whom he had met at his aunt's soirées), and the themes of spirit, music, decay and sensuality are all present in his later works, and expressed still more clearly in his Funerary Suites of the 1830s.

In the original the writing itself is brown, and the paper is blotched with a number of brown stains, smudged by the hand. For many years it was thought that Sudbury had written these verses in either his own or Brandy's blood, but forensic analysis, generously conducted by the Institute of Forensic Science on our behalf in 1998, has revealed that it was in fact written using particularly strong coffee. (On the standard Viennese cup measure of the period this would equate to 167.2 beans per cup – at the same time, Ludwig van Beethoven, a man known for the intensity of his spirit, was obsessing upon the perfect cup of coffee, and insisted upon counting out sixty beans per cup. It can therefore be concluded that Sudbury probably liked a considerably stronger cup of coffee than Beethoven.)

23. An example of Sudbury's thumbprint on the manuscript of the poem.

Another exciting discovery on this manuscript was the profusion of finger and thumbprints present throughout the many pages. These clearly demonstrate that he had unusually thick fingers for a man of his stature, which may account for the proliferation of double stopped fifths in his music, an interval that many violinists with normal or thin fingers find particularly difficult to pitch exactly.

The few accounts that we have of this period of his life, written by his friend, Oswald Camberley, a Freemason and amateur sportsman, in a series of unpublished letters to William Beckford (who had asked him to keep an eye on Sudbury), paint a vivid picture of the despair into which he had fallen:

12th February 1827

… Against my better judgement, I went to visit Charles again at Cadogan Square. On my previous visit he had chased me from the building, screaming obscenities in a most disreputable manner, and openly displaying his nakedness as his dressing gown billowed out behind him. It was a most embarrassing scene, and one which was unfortunately reported in the local broadsheets. Yet I held within my breast such sorrow for what had become of him that I felt the need to offer what comfort I could, despite my many reservations.

Upon entering his rooms it was clear that the mania had at last left him, to be replaced by a profound and stagnant gloom, which expressed itself in every aspect of his surroundings. The curtains had obviously not been opened in months, and the air was filled with the sour stench of pipe smoke and various rotting things that are best left undescribed. Charles lay, pale and withered, upon the couch, covered by numerous mismatched blankets and furs, and shivering emphatically whilst mumbling to himself. He seemed barely aware of my presence. All around him lay the evidence of his dark mentality: bottles of all shapes and sizes, many of them empty of the laudanum and brandy they had once contained; papers written upon in great haste, filled with blotches and scribblings that were barely decipherable; plates covered with the decayed remains of what may have once been food, but now would pass for little more than sludge and slime: it was truly a deplorable and saddening sight.

After a momentary attempt at tidying that soon revealed its own absurdity, I resolved to leave and make haste to Dr Sanders where I arranged, at some considerable expense, to have the good doctor look in upon him daily, and let me know of his progress. This having been agreed, we settled down to a fine game of poker, in which I am glad to say I made back much of my money, and concluded the evening with the finest Scotch whisky I have tasted in many long years ...

In a later letter, dated 1 March, it is clear that Sudbury's physical condition had improved, though his mind was still suffering from paranoid delusions, which were to plague him, in various degrees, for the rest of his life:

Charles is looking much better, though he still refuses to leave his rooms. Dr Sanders had arranged, some weeks ago, for Mrs Trowbridge to return, as Charles had dismissed her in December, and as a result the rooms are at least in good order now, though I had to pay her a not inconsiderable sum to reconsider working for Charles after the manner in which he had treated her, and more still, to attempt the initial cleansing (I enclose the necessary accounts and politely await recompense).

What concerns me most is his mental state – he seems to pass from lucid to utterly delusional in an instant, without the slightest warning, and though no longer violent, his eyes bear witness to the intensity of turmoil that lurks within him. The most vehement of his verbal venom is reserved for 'the Catholics', whom he accuses of everything from being 'the destroyers of men's souls', to having a personal vendetta against him. However, when I persuaded him to take up his violin and play me the piece he was working on, I was entirely astonished. Never had I before heard such music, nor such playing, as if the depths to which he had so recently sunk had only served to show him the way to an essence of intensity heretofore unknown. Verily he must suredly be the most sombre and sonorous violinist in all of England…

During this period of illness he had refused many requests for his funerary services, amongst them a request from William, Duke of Clarence (George IV's younger brother and heir presumptive to the throne), to perform at the funeral of Edward Devin, a snub that William would remember when he became king in 1830.

By June 1827 Sudbury had recovered much of his health and returned to performing. A change in him was noted by many, who would comment upon the 'wild look' in his eyes and his 'brusque and, at times, un-gentlemanly manner', but acknowledged that his playing had 'clearly traversed the depths of Hell, and brought back upon its ever brooding melancholy melodies a knowledge of the secrets of the damned, too darkly profound for the comprehension of ordinary men' (Oswald Camberley, 27 June 1827).

The following two years ostensibly brought a continuation of Sudbury's popular success, and demand for his services was once again increasing, as were his fees (and the number of myths and rumours that were rapidly growing up around his eccentric behaviour). His mind was slowly settling, and reports of his outbursts became less frequent, though they never disappeared altogether. His insistence on never speaking directly before, during or after a funerary performance did much to disguise the extent of his many inner conflicts, and a fragile sanity was regained. It was also during this time that he began to consolidate his Funerary Aesthetic (a semi-religious music-based mysticism linking the funerary performance with the calling up and cleansing of souls), which was to grow throughout the 1830s into something of a cult, with many pretenders and charlatans following in its wake.

On 26 September 1829, Sudbury's mentor, and President of the Guild of Funerary Violinists, Joseph Beckham, died suddenly in a carriage accident whilst travelling from Epping to London during a severe storm. (When his body was found it had been stripped of all clothing and possessions by thieves, and as a result it was six days before he was identified – his violin, a fine instrument by Daniel Parker c. 1720, with an original death's head scroll carved by the maker, has never been found.) More recently, scholars have suggested that the death of Beckham may have been one of the first assassinations of the Great Funerary Purges, but as yet no definite evidence has been discovered. It is thought such evidence may exist in the archives of the Vatican, though they have denied all knowledge.

As Secretary to the Guild, and its most famous member, it was inevitable that Sudbury would be elected President, and his first duty was to perform at the interment of his predecessor in the churchyard of St Martin's in the Fields on 5 October 1829. He was officially welcomed as the incoming President on 1 November, at the Guild's headquarters in Cavendish Square. We are fortunate that he included the speech he gave on the occasion in his *Considerations of the Funerary Arts* and, in addition, that the pages on which it appears were amongst those found intact amidst the ashes of the fire that destroyed the Guild's headquarters in 1841; the fire in which Sudbury himself was to die. This speech gives us a fascinating insight into the evolving spiritual philosophy that was beginning to dominate Sudbury's life and performances, and I therefore quote it in full:

Gentlemen, that music is the oldest and most subtle of all the noble Arts has long been the accepted and expounded philosophy of every cultured man; but the means or magic by which it weaves its enchantments are as unknown and misunderstood today as were the miracles of gunpowder and silk to our distant forebears. Though its motion is entirely invisible, yet it holds the power to stir the soul without the slightest physical touch: more comforting than a mother's smile; more sensual than a lover's embrace; more richly filled with dreams than an apothecary's chest; it holds within its grasp the power to uplift the individual spirit and to change the course of nations.

In the beginning we were all of nought but mud, and God's own breath blew life into our un-pumping hearts: but what is breath but vibrations in the air, and what are such vibrations but the means and form of music? The Greeks knew this secret – for music was the Art of their Gods: did not Apollo play upon a lyre? and Pan upon a set of pipes? For music is the very breath of life, the very language of God through which he speaks to us of Godly things, of things intangible to mortal language, yet universally perceived by all whose souls have but a spark of holiness within.

And is not Man the most blessed of all God's beasts, wherein he has been given the freedom to make of God's own breath what he will? For the thrush has but one song to sing, and the starling can but imitate and not invent: Man alone can thread the subtle notes where e'er he will, and make of it a wondrous thing.

Certainly each part within our world is part of God; each living beast, each plant and rock and stream is but a vessel for the Lord, and would but cease were it not so. Certainly a swan begets a swan, a snail begets a snail, a worm begets a worm, and that is evidence enough of the presence of the Lord within: but Man's many children take on every form – there is nought yet conceived that we cannot make into a figment of our own reality, thanks to the gift of the breath of God.

Is not the art of speech a form of music? Are not poetry, philosophy, mathematics, geometry, and astrology, all in their way a single strand of the great cloth of music? For music is the very breath of life, and in taking form it builds the bridge between that which is merely conceived, and that which can truly be attained.

And herein lies the pith of it: that our relationship with that which lies in everything, the true and single Spirit of the Lord, has been stolen by word-ridden priests whose preaching smothers like a blindfold the common sense of all mankind. For surely, where a priest can but interpret ancient words and call them Truth, the humblest of musicians does converse with the Lord in every minute spent devoted to his art, in every note he draws from deep within his soul.

This savage usurpment of the Truth of God, though no more than pretence and clever words, has deceived us all for far too long. For are not words, and the many misunderstandings which they carry in their wake, the cause of every war? the tool through which injustices of every kind are not only meted out, but carried like wildfire upon the wind, to every hidden corner of our world?

Is not language limited within itself? There are no words that truly render Love, nor Beauty, nor Faith, nor God to those who do not yet share the vision. But pass to me my violin and I will show the very heart of each and every one of them.

These priests, these bold pretenders, these poachers in the garden of the Lord, would have us bow and scrape to them, as if to God himself, whilst they baffle us with nonsensical and convoluted discourses, calculated to plunder both our pockets and our hearts. They have railed against musicians, condemning them with all the cunning vacillations of a she-fox, since the day of the destruction of the Hebrews' second temple. And why this insidious fear and loathing of those who move the soul without words? Because they know that music holds the power, in a single well-judged note, to wholly dispel the aura of deific majesty they work so hard to cultivate.

You might ask: And what of it? Are they not like any other power in the world, cheating and deceiving their way through life to line their pockets and maintain their hold on those off whom they live? Are they not as the knights and knaves of old? Is there not a need for order in the world? Is not man's role to suffer at the hands of other men? Is not justice a concept that belongs to God alone? You might ask all these things, and rightly so. And truly I am not concerned with life's many swindlers and deceivers. So what if they dress up their words in a pretence of holiness? It is no different from whoever took that place before, nor whoever stands in line.

My concern lies wholly in the final and most sinful of their many bold conceits. For it is my certainty that the Last Rites is no more than a conceit, contrived over the centuries to conjure up a final burst of generosity towards the church, in exchange for God's own guarantee of Salvation. But surely heaven cannot be entered upon a lie. To stride towards the Gates with falsely given confidence is Sin in itself, and whilst the Church's reward may be material, what they are stealing is, for their naïve victim, Eternity itself. Think on the millions that have thus been damned. Think on the scale of it. The infiniteness of the tragedy is too large for the mind of man to conceive.

And yet I come back to the Breath of God that was given to Man in the Spirit of Music. For though it has not the power to resurrect the body once its task is done; in the hands of a Godly master, well versed in the sacred secret rites of Funerary Violin, it can draw up the Soul from its purgatorial torment, and send it, through a ritual of confession and atonement, cleansed of all Sin, to sit beside the Lord on high. Have we the right to reject this gift, now that it is given? Surely we are duty bound to raise our violins to God with every beat upon our hearts, with every single breath, and play with all the morbid subtlety our very Souls can muster, to demonstrate our Faith, and purify the many generations that the priests have left below without a thought. With such a gift comes grave responsibility. We must take the Art of Funerary Violin to every house of God, to every churchyard, and pray with all the music we can muster, for the many lost souls who are doomed to drift for all eternity without our intervention.

The Funerary Violinist is the bringer of peace to those who have only torment; the saver of Souls to those who have no power to save themselves; the purveyor of life to those who see only death and darkness; the focus of hearts that long to weep, but have for many years been nought but dust; the bringer of dreams to the sleepless, food to the hungerless, air to the breath-less: we hold the very Fate of Man in our violins.

A number of themes run through this speech, which were to become central to Sudbury's Funerary Aesthetic: the notion that music holds within it the power to resurrect the soul and somehow cleanse it of its sins; the hatred and distrust of Catholics, whom he was to blame for not only all the sins of man, but also the 'savage repression of the dead'; an ever-increasing self-importance and self-justi-fication in which he would become the hero of his own delusions; and an un-doubted talent for poetical rhetoric, which he was to use throughout the 1830s to raise the status of Funerary Violin and build up a cult of followers throughout England.

The death of George IV, on 26 June 1830, was to have a major influence on the course of Sudbury's career. Despite his dislike of the 'fatuous oaf', Sudbury had found that being in the King's favour made a major contribution towards his standing, not only within the Guild but amongst the Freemasons and in high society as a whole. The accession of William IV was to change much of that. George IV had died an unpopular king, renowned for his extravagance and gluttony. William was quite the opposite: unassuming, discouraging of pomp and ceremony – and he had not forgotten Sudbury's snub of 1827. Since the reign of Charles II, it had been traditional for the President of the Guild of Funerary Violinists to perform publicly at the funeral of any 'persons of great note or standing', and especially of royalty. These performances were always by order of the Crown, unlike those for 'persons of some, but not considerable, note', at whose funerals the Secretary to the Guild would perform, which were arranged by the Privy Council. This put William IV officially in charge of all such requests for Sudbury to perform, a situation that would have many ramifications for the musician over the coming years.

The first sign of this change in fortune came on 15 July with the funeral of George IV. Sudbury was informed that he would not be required to perform at the funeral, and after some negotiations it was decided he would play to the body later that

24. The interior of St George's Chapel, Windsor, where, over a period of nearly 200 years, Funerary Violinists were to perform for the corpses of many of England's greatest monarchs. Charles Sudbury was to be the last such artist heard in the building when he played for the body of George IV in 1830; however, by then the Art was already falling out of favour and this final performance took place underneath the floor of the chapel, in the Royal Mausoleum below.

evening in the crypt of St George's Chapel, at Windsor Castle (which turned out to be something of a blessing as George IV was not a popular king, and faeces were hurled at the coffin all along the route). That was to be the last official state Funerary Violin performance Sudbury, or anyone, was to give, for William had announced that he was to cut down considerably on royal spending, and amongst his many budget cuts and diminutions of pomp and ceremony was the abolition of all state-funded performances of Funerary Violin.

Sudbury turned this change of function to his advantage: no longer tied to the state, nor on call to anyone, he devoted himself to both composing and proselytising. In March 1830 he embarked on his first major tour of England, stopping at St Albans, Bedford, Northampton, Leicester, Nottingham, Mansfield, Chesterfield, Sheffield, Huddersfield, Manchester, Liverpool, Chester, Crewe, Shrewsbury, Wolverhampton, Birmingham, Kidderminster, Worcester, Cheltenham, Stroud, Bristol, Bath, Salisbury, Southampton, Portsmouth, Worthing and Brighton, and finally returning to London after a full thirteen months on the road. Though this was his longest tour, he took to the road a further two times during the 1830s.

His method was straightforward. Travelling with a friend or colleague, and at times with the Guild's Secretary, Matthew Connisten (appointed Secretary by Sudbury upon his taking up the presidency), he would arrive in a town, armed with his official documentation, and hastily arrange a public lecture (usually in the town hall, or a large church) entitled 'A Defence of the Art of Funerary Violin'. Posters would be put up at strategic places around the town advertising the lecture three days before, and to attract further interest Sudbury would give spontaneous concerts for the dead at midnight in local graveyards on each of the previous evenings. A typical example of the lecture itself is included in his *Considerations of the Funerary Arts*, though its similarity to the speech he gave upon receiving the presidency makes it unnecessary to quote it here.

After the lecture he would stay in the town for up to a week and, almost without fail, would be called upon to perform at upcoming funerals or memorial services, which gave him an opportunity to demonstrate the Art, about which he had spoken so passionately. In this way he was able to raise the profile of Funerary Violin amongst the populace who, in many towns, had only heard the village coffin-maker's attempts at fulfilling the role. Sudbury was horrified to discover the inadequacy of standards amongst regional Funerary Violinists, and even more so to find that in some towns the tradition had been entirely lost. He soon began to set up auditions for apprentices whom he would send to London to study with members of the Guild at his own expense, and by 1840 their number had reached eighty-two.

Upon his return to London in April 1831, Sudbury found that his graveyard concerts and proselytising had created quite a momentary stir amongst the higher echelons of society, and he was once again a figure of noted celebrity, much talked of in the local broadsheets, and caricatured by many pamphleteers. In his *Considerations* he writes:

> *I had become quite the hero of the day, they were calling me The Dark Lord of the Violin, and some even claimed that I dined with the Grim Reaper every night.*

But his moment of glory was shattered on 3 June 1831, when Paganini gave his first concert in England, at the King's Theatre in Haymarket.

For the previous 250 years the only formal situation in which a solo violin was played in public had been that of the funeral. Hence the Funerary Violinist held sway over the solitary melancholic tones that have such power to move the spirit and imagination. Now, for the first time, the venerable tradition had a challenger: a miraculous Italian for whom the word virtuoso seemed altogether too limiting. *The Times* gave a typical review of that first concert:

> *Nothing can be more difficult than to describe Paganini's performance on the violin, so as to make the effect of it intelligible to those who have never heard him … He is not only the finest player perhaps who has ever existed on that instrument, but he forms a class by himself, and produces effects which he has been the first to discover, and in which few, if any imitators will be able to follow.*

In addition, since 1824 Paganini had made it his habit to give free concerts in local cemeteries and graveyards for those who could not afford to see him in the concert halls (he always doubled the house prices wherever he played, and these free concerts were a way of defusing any local bad feeling). Although he was a little disappointed with the lack of grandeur in English churchyards, as they did not compare to the Venice Lido or Père-Lachaise, he continued with these unadvertised 'Poor Concerts', which, in combination with Sudbury's recent tour, created no little degree of confusion amongst both contemporary writers and the public as to which was related to the tradition of Funerary Violin. Ultimately, the resulting debate created a fashion for graveyard concerts all over the country, with many poor or mediocre players misusing the Funerary Violin tradition as a means to generate publicity and further their own flagging careers.

By 1832 it seemed that every graveyard had acquired its own imitators. From virtuosi to the most humble of village fiddlers, everyone was putting on spontaneous 'Funerarianas', as they soon became known as. Crowds would gather in the early evening, small stall holders would set up offering food and other refreshments (by 1833 it was not uncommon for tents to be put up by entrepreneurs offering a little privacy for 'gentlemen's activities') and white face-paint, worn in fashionable imitation of the famous Herr Gratchenfleiss, abounded. The music would not start until dusk, though it soon became apparent that music was not really any longer an important part of the proceedings. Sir John Asquith of North Street, Brighton, records, in an unpublished diary, a fascinating description of just such a scene on 17 November 1833, in the grounds of St Nicholas church:

> *After a tiresome afternoon with Miss Dutton, a woman as ugly as she is rich, I felt in dire need of spiritual invigoration and so decided to attend the evening's Funerariana. The concert was to be given by Mr Schultz, a visiting minor soloist from Munich (or so he claims, though rumour has it that he speaks with a Birmingham accent), and the occasional phrases I heard wafting among the crowds were indeed acceptable. I am much enamoured of the current fashion for white faces at these events; it can cover even the most virulent of poxes, and makes the many solicitous young ladies most irresistible. Met Tibbles and thoroughly beat him at Nudge. Had a most satisfying rummaging amongst the skirts with a delightful Miss of Welsh origin, before hiring one of Higley's tents, right next to the grave of Sir Robert Bolingbrook.*

It is clear from this document, now held in the British Library, that what had started as a sincere expression of artistic values, by both Sudbury and Paganini, had quickly sunk into decadence. Sudbury reacted with typical tempestuous vigour by embarking on a second tour of England, in May 1833, this time proselytising against the noble Art's many imitators. In his *Considerations* he includes a copy of this lecture, from which the following extracts are taken:

> *It has come to my attention, in the wake of the recent successes of Maestro Paganini, combined with the many rumours that surround him, associating him with demonic and occult practices (particularly regarding his unsolic-*

ited performances in many churchyards), that a fashion has arisen for the cheap imitation of the Funerary Violinist, by those who are wholly unqualified. And indeed we at the Guild of Funerary Violinists must shoulder some of the blame, for we have, for far too long, been far too secretive about the sacred nature of our vocation, and in doing so, have laid ourselves open to many misrepresentations, and misunderstandings by a public that has no cause to know any better.

In an effort to address these pale pretenders, and awaken the populace from their solemnly enforced ignorance, I have been persuaded to reveal at least some of our less sacred practices, that the people should learn to distinguish the true Funerary Violinist from the many fakers whose graveyard performances are in every sense a mockery of God's own law.

A Funerary Violinist does not give concerts, nor charge a public fee – he appears by prior arrangement to commend the soul of the dead to God. He does not wear a periwig, nor paint his face, nor should he bear any ostentatious outward sign of his mortal trade, save the black ribbon tied around the scroll of his violin, as a symbol of the exclusive nature of his performances, which are for the dead alone – though, of course, the living are always in mild attendance …

For many years it was the custom for the apprentice, upon conferment of his title of mastership, to have the scroll of his violin re-carved by a local luthier to resemble a Death's Head. In some cases these subtle Death's Head scrolls have been passed through the generations, but the practice fell out of favour many years ago, and the monstrous modern gothic carvings seen in the hands of many complicitous rascals today, are no more than comical mimicry …

A Funerary Suite must always have seven distinct movements; seven being the number of sacred completion; representing the seventh day of rest, and the seven seals of judgement day. Of these, three should be marches, in one or other form: the first to accompany the body to the church, the second to escort the body from the church to the grave, and the third as a solemn reminder of the sacred brevity of life. These are the functional aspects of the suite. The remaining four movements should be a flight, a panic, a dream, and a eulogy. The spiritual intention behind these pieces must remain a *secret of the initiated, and any who talk too freely of these things can be easily seen for the charlatans they must inevitably be ...*

Because its main aim was the disavowing of charlatans and pretenders, this second lecture tour was shorter than the previous one, as Sudbury had no great need to stay for any duration in a town. He did, however, make a point of protesting and spreading leaflets outside Funerarianas if he came upon them, and giving his own Concerts for the Dead as a demonstration of the true spirit of his art. He arrived back in London in February 1834, utterly exhausted both mentally and physically, and retreated to his rooms in Cadogan Square. What was initially exhaustion compounded with heavy drinking soon turned into pneumonia, and it was a further six months before, under the care of Dr Sanders, he slowly regained some, if not all, of his former strength.

On the orders of Dr Percival Sanders (son of Dr Theodore Sanders, who had taken over his father's practice in 1829 after Theodore had suffered a near-fatal cerebral aneurysm), he withdrew from public life for the following eighteen months, only giving the occasional performance when requested to by a friend or fellow Free-mason. He spent much of his time alone in his rooms, behind closed curtains, absorbed in attempting to realise his vision of the seven-movement Funerary Suite, until, in a speech to the board of the Guild in September 1835, upon his return to the position of President (the Acting Presidency having been taken over by Connisten in his absence), he announced the composition of 'ten new Funerary Suites, intricately calculated to raise up the spirit of the recently dead, and send them, fully cleansed, unto the embrace of our Holy Father'. We cannot say for certain whether these suites were ever performed in a funerary context, but it seems likely that they would have been, at the funerals of John Loudon McAdam (1836), Charles Simeon (1836), Sir John Soane (1837) and Joseph Lancaster (1838) (amongst other less notable persons), all of whom were fellow members of the Grand Lodge, and all of whom had specifically requested that Sudbury should perform at their interments.

In 1837 King William IV died, and to return the long-standing insult, though Sudbury was asked by the Privy Council to perform at his funeral, he refused on the polite grounds of ill health ('the very thought of him made me evacuate my bowels!' – *Considerations of the Funerary Arts*). William had so successfully demolished the previously long-standing relationship between the Guild and the Crown that it was no surprise that his even more frugal niece, Queen Victoria, did nothing to reinstate it; and so the change of monarch brought little change to Sudbury's position nor that of the Guild itself.

The year 1837 did, however, herald storm clouds from another direction altogether. Scholars are, as yet, uncertain of the specific causes of the Great Funerary Purges, and many varied arguments have been posited and discredited over time. It is, of course, possible that the answer lies in the archives of the Vatican, and that one day these archives will reveal their secrets, but officially the Vatican has always denied all knowledge of the events. The issues involved together with current theories are gone into in more detail in the Guild's publication *The Great Funerary Purges*; however, here we will confine ourselves to how this historical eradication of a once great musical and spiritual culture was to effect Sudbury, and the Guild of Funerary Violinists itself.

It is not known exactly when the Great Funerary Purge crossed the English Channel, as its initial efforts were both cunning and subtle. However, it had been spreading across Europe steadily since 1833, originating in orders from Rome itself. The often unnoticed disappearance of books from libraries and private collections was followed by a series of apparently unconnected burglaries around the country: paintings of Funerary Violinists were taken; old violins with the traditional death's head scrolls were either vandalised or stolen; and pamphlets were circulated that condemned Funerary Violin as 'the music of the Devil'. But by July 1837 these many diverse and seemingly unconnected events were forming a pattern, and on 26 July a meeting of the board of the Guild was called. It was Matthew Connisten, the Secretary to the Guild, who had first noticed the pattern and put it together with the many rumours that were coming from Europe of similar, and more serious, events. He gave a thorough report of his suspicions, listings all of the sinisterly innocuous crimes (a list sadly now lost), and suggested that there was some kind of conspiracy brewing against the Guild and its followers. Sudbury's typical and vehement response was that it was:

> all down to that heaving multiplicity of Antichrists, the Catholics, who have not the courage to stand proudly in pursuit of their manifold crimes, but slither on their bellies that they may conduct their evil business unseen, and also be closer to their Lord and Master in Hell!
>
> (Considerations of the Funerary Arts)

That Sudbury was, on this occasion, correct in his suspicion of the Catholic Church's complicity in these events, was, of course, no more than coincidence (he had been subject to delusions of Catholic persecution since he was nineteen), though at the time it led to his being credited with the gift of foresight – a myth that persisted throughout much of the nineteenth century, and was particularly potent during the 1880s and 1890s when there was a great revival of interest in the more 'Spiritualist' side of his Funerary Aesthetic. (Madame Blavatsky, founder of the Theosophical movement, was the last person to attempt to commission a Funerary Suite from him, in 1889, although seemingly the message did not get through to the other side as no suite was forthcoming.)

With the renewed vigour of a man who has been proven right after many years of being considered paranoid, Sudbury retired to his rooms once again to consolidate his ideas and writings, and by January 1838 he had compiled the first draft of *Considerations of the Funerary Arts,* a book he was to continue amending until his death in 1841. Having completed what he called this 'representation of my life, my thoughts, my visions and my fears', he embarked upon his final tour of England, this time with an agenda that included revealing the Catholic conspiracy to the world, and forewarning those whom he considered likely targets.

However, Britain had entered more tolerant times (the Catholic Emancipation Act of 1829 had legally underlined a new mood of religious equality), and Sudbury's repeated verbal attacks upon the Catholic Church were now considered incitement to civil disorder, attracting the attentions of the government. On 3 April 1838, at a meeting of the Grand Lodge of London, the issue of Sudbury's 'anti-tolerant' behaviour was officially raised, in his absence. Despite an emphatic and emotional justification of his actions by Connisten (which is recorded in the minutes of the meeting), Sudbury was dishonourably cast out of the Freemasons, on the grounds of 'bringing shame and disgrace upon the Lodge by association', leaving him, for the first time, with very few powerful friends, and as a result he soon found many doors closing to him.

By June 1838 his lecture tour was becoming a disaster. He was no longer able to find a companion willing to travel with him, and increasingly, upon his arrival in a town, he was greeted by a delegation from the local Lodge making it clear that his presence was not welcome. In July he abandoned the tour altogether, returning directly to London, where he arrived on 5 August and immediately called for a meeting of the Guild, which was held on 10 August, and was to be the last publicly acknowledged meeting of the Board of Directors. Much to his relief the Guild remained loyal, being all too aware of the truth behind his words, but rather than attacking the issue head on, as Sudbury would, they resolved to temporarily withdraw from public view, and the committee was officially dissolved, in the hope that a subtle retreat might halt the escalating persecution being levelled against them. Deeply hurt and disappointed, and suffering from severe emotional and physical exhaustion, Sudbury retreated once again to his rooms in Cadogan Square, where he continued to work on his *Considerations.* William Beckford, his long-term patron, had withdrawn his annuity under pressure from the Grand Lodge, but by now Sudbury had become wealthy in his own right, and this retracting of what had always been promised as a lifelong pension, was more of a social snub than a financial inconvenience.

Little is known of the following two years, as much of the evidence that we have about Sudbury comes either from his *Considerations* (a book that only covers the years up to 1838), or from Guild records, which ceased to be officially kept after the meeting of 10 August. Connisten kept some records, particularly regarding the increasing number of attacks upon Guild property and its members, and though unsubstantiated by any other source, they make a disturbing account of a period of fear and repression that has now been almost entirely forgotten. The specific details of this account are considered more thoroughly in the Guild's publication *The Great Funerary Purges*, but it is of relevance here to summarise some of the more serious incidents.

According to Connisten, what had started in 1836 as little more than a series of petty crimes including burglary and vandalism escalated in April 1839 to involve attacks on Guild members. The first such attack was against Thomas Goldsmith, 1st Funerary Violinist to the Parish of Southwark, on 12 April, and left him with two broken wrists. Between that date and December 1841 (a date beyond which I am obliged not to refer), he details forty-two such incidents, each involving Guild members and each resulting in broken hands or arms, and on three occasions the subsequent death of the victim. In February 1840, the first of twelve mysterious disappearances occurred when Percy Winthrop, previously a Guild Committee member, failed to return from a visit to the Inns of Court; and on 7 December 1840, the first of a series of fires at offices of the Guild broke out in Cambridge.

On 22 February 1841 a fire of unknown origin started in the basement of the Guild's headquarters at 17 Cavendish Square, and by 3 a.m. had spread to the ground floor. Word was sent to Sudbury, who arrived at the scene at approximately 3.45 a.m., and on seeing the smoke billowing from the lower windows, immediately rushed inside to save what he could of his own work and the Guild's historical

25. Charles Sudbury photographed here in 1841, less than a month before his death in a fire at the offices of the Guild. The egoistic mania that ultimately led to his demise is clearly evident in his wild staring eyes and clenched jaw.

archives. He was never seen alive again. Connisten reports how the remains of his body were found the next day, amidst a pile of beams and smouldering ashes, and upon the body's being lifted, there was discovered underneath him a number of books and documents that had remained largely undamaged, amongst them a copy of his own *Considerations,* and a number of pages from the 1697 edition of *The Erroneous Dirges of George Babcotte*. Sadly, most of the archives were completely destroyed, and Connisten spent many hours sifting through the wreckage to salvage what he could. It is largely thanks to his efforts that we know what we do of the Guild's Venerable History. It is not known for certain whether Sudbury's interment (in the newly established Highgate Cemetery) was accompanied by a Funerary Violinist as no record of the event has as yet been discovered. However, it is likely that Connisten would have performed, as tradition dictated.

That same night, in his absence, Sudbury's rooms had been raided and all of his writings and music, together with his collection of violins, had been taken, making the fifty or so pages of his *Considerations of the Funerary Arts* that were rescued by Connisten the only surviving copy, and as such one of the Guild's most valuable and tantalising documents. Without it we would have scant knowledge of Sudbury's life, and know virtually nothing of the fascinating workings of his mind and the complex and profound Funerary Aesthetic that he evolved throughout his turbulent years; we would know little of the relationship between the Guild of Funerary Violinists and the Grand Lodge of London, and still less of Sudbury's vehement anti-Catholicism, which some scholars believe to have been a contributing factor to the ferocity of the Funerary Purges in England. The Guild is intending to publish a facsimile edition of this most valuable and fascinating of documents in the near future. However, urgent conservation work must be carried out first, and until that is done it is impossible to estimate when such a publication will be available.

26. & 27. Charles Sudbury's sadly neglected grave, which can be found in the far north-west corner of Highgate West Cemetery. As he had, by the time of his death, long since lost contact with his surviving family, and also fallen out with most of his own friends and colleagues, his grave soon fell into disrepair. His brief popular revival in the 1880s led to this spot becoming something of a tourist attraction, and as such the grave was cleared and restored in 1881. However, a further century of failing interest has once again left it overgrown and in danger of collapse.

Some Brief Comments On The Music

It is a tragedy that only one of the Funerary Suites composed in 1835 has survived. Entitled *Funerary Suite no. 4,* it was found in an attic in Lansdowne Terrace, Bath, in 1920 (where William Beckford had retired in 1829). The music clearly demonstrates a profound influence from Herr Gratchenfleiss, but is more considered and better ordered. It fulfils all the correct criteria as laid out in the *Considerations,* being in seven movements, with three Marches, a Panic, a Flight, a Dream and a Eulogy, and though Sudbury cannot be credited with inventing these forms, since they all have precedents in the works of Herr Gratchenfleiss and earlier, he was amongst the first (together with Pierre Dubuisson) to gather them together into a structured suite. The *Funerary Suite no. 4* is amongst the best examples of the form. The pieces themselves are more harmonic than is typical of the prevalent eighteenth- and early nineteenth-century style, and Sudbury has stretched the definition of a March to mean 'a piece in a solid walking pace', no longer limited to 4/4 time or the simple repetitive tunes usually associated with the term. The spiritual and ritual intentions of the movements are hinted at in the subtitles:

1. *March – For the subtle approach of Death: to ease the fear and calm the Soul's gentle mortification.*
2. *Introduction and March – To show the Soul's newfound delight, and expel the sadness of those who mourn.*
3. *Dream – As the Soul looks down upon all that is laid aside, a brief moment of grief before the bargaining begins.*
4. *Panic – For the banishment of all spirits whose heart is not of purest white, and to drive away the evil-minded ghosts that dwell where death is to be found.*
5. *Flight – As if to dispel all doubts, the cleansed Spirit marks a final path between God and Man, before its ultimate ascension.*
6. *Eulogy – A final farewell as the Spirit rises unto God; not without sadness we put our faith, and the spirit of our dead, in God's own hands.*
7. *March – Now that all is done and as it should be, we may weep without reserve.*

Unfortunately there is no more detailed description of the ritual intentions behind these works, and though there may have been references to them in the pages of the *Considerations* that were destroyed in the fire, many scholars now believe that to be unlikely, as Sudbury's known writings all remain cryptically secretive about the specific details ('The spiritual intention behind these pieces must remain a secret of the initiated, and any who talk too freely of these things can be easily seen for the charlatans they must inevitably be ... ').

The extent to which this and Sudbury's other Funerary Suites would have been a profound influence on the evolution of the genre as a whole can only be guessed at, since not only was this work lost for eighty years, but by the time it was rediscovered the whole tradition had been forced to a sudden and brutal conclusion. The fact that what little we do know of Sudbury is dependent upon so few extant documents is testament to the huge body of knowledge, history and art that was forever destroyed in the Great Funerary Purges, and we can but hope that one day much that was stolen will be slowly unearthed, and the great and venerable history of the Art of Funerary Violin may be rediscovered and brought into the light, that we all may benefit, once again, from its profound and sonorous tones.

28. With the emergence of Spiritualism and Theosophy as popular movements in the 1880s, Charles Sudbury once again caught the public imagination. Briefly hailed as a misunderstood prophet, his works, particularly the *Considerations of the Funerary Arts*, and his Funerary Suite no. 4 became the often unmentioned inspiration behind many pieces of music, poems and paintings of the time, such as this affectionate caricature: 'Sudbury Still Conjuring His Ghosts', by L. Wendell, 1885.

Matthew Connisten

A Brief Tribute to a Singularly Methodical Man

29. Matthew Connisten c. 1845

It is well known that history can be unkind, and particularly the history of art – so dominated by the half-mad and the reckless – which by its nature seeks the supermen whose vision spurns the everyday, and rarely takes the time to cast a glance on those diligent and methodical men without whom so much would have been forever lost. And so it has always been for Matthew Connisten. Eternally beshadowed by his fiery predecessor Charles Sudbury, Connisten's own small contribution to our noble history was neither creative nor passionate, and yet, had he been a different kind of man – a man, say, of greater vigour and lesser patience – we can be certain that both the Guild of Funerary Violinists and its archive would have long since sunk into the mud of time without a trace. Indeed, much of what we know of the Great Funerary Purges, and their tragic manifestation in England, comes from Connisten's own heroic efforts at book-keeping during the period, and it was he who turned the Guild from a proud and public proponent of its Art, into the secretive and, some would say, paranoid organisation that has survived to this day against all odds.

And yet here I am obliged to stop and consider: for to present Connisten and his many near-monumental achievements during his eighteen years as President of the Guild (1841–59) would be to go against everything that he worked so hard towards. As I said in the foreword to this book, I am obligated to mention little of the Guild and its working after 1841, and the 'New and Secretive Way' as instigated by Connisten is amongst those things that are to be kept most secret. However, to provide a history of the Art without mentioning Connisten's valiant efforts to preserve our legacy at all costs would seem ridiculous as he was, after all, one of the great Presidents of the Guild, if not the best of musicians.

There is little to mention of note in Connisten's period as Secretary under Sudbury that was not mentioned in the previous chapter. He was certainly a great supporter of Sudbury, and took over the Acting Presidency during Sudbury's many 'illnesses'; it has indeed been suggested that, were it not for Connisten's support, Sudbury might have been ousted by the more conservative members of the board as early as 1830, when some of his more unconventional attitudes were starting to reveal themselves. But it was not until the hours after Sudbury's death that Connisten proved his mettle and set the tone for his future Presidency, for it was Connisten who braved the embers to save what remained of the Guild's archives, including many of the works that remain today amongst the central canon of the Art of Funerary Violin; it was also Connisten who began keeping records of the many crimes against the Guild during the Great Funerary Purges, working out patterns to aid in the escape from further danger. Though these records remain beyond the public domain, they do indeed make a compelling case against the many agents of the Vatican involved, for various reasons, in actions against the Guild during this time.

30. Matthew Connisten (on the right) photographed in 1885 in his
official capacity as 1st Mute. The strain of his eighteen years as
President of the Guild is clearly evident in his shrunken frame.
Meticulous and secretive by nature, he found here at last, one cannot
help but think, his ideal profession. (The man on his left is thought to
be his nephew, Edgar Connisten.)

Though I am both unable and, in part, unwilling to discuss the years 1841–59,
during which, under Connisten's leadership, the Guild radically reorganised itself into
a very different kind of organisation, I am nonetheless profoundly indebted to his
tremendous talent as a record keeper and maker of lists, and that I am writing this book
at all is a testament to the ultimate success of his vocation as preserver of the Art.

Amongst the handful of compositions that he left (he was one of the slowest of all
composers), the only set of any note is the *Introduction, Dirge and March* com-

posed to the memory of Charles Sudbury. Initially he was planning a seven-movement Funerary Suite, in the manner that Sudbury had dictated, but after nearly four years he finally accepted his lack of fluency and left it as a three-movement work. Although the music lacks many of the requisite features of a true funerary work, it is not without some charm. The 'Introduction' quotes the *Dies Irae* monody that is more often associated with the classical expression of mortality, and the March itself is diligently repetitive.

Connisten retired from the Presidency in 1859, at the age of only fifty, on the grounds of increasing ill health. It is thought that he set up a boarding house in Piccadilly and had nothing further to do with the Guild or its members. However, it is clear that he missed the atmosphere of a good funeral, as in 1870 he became 3rd Mute (official mourner) to Alfred Morgan, Undertaker, by Appointment to Her Majesty Queen Victoria, situated off the Strand, and by 1885 he had risen to the position of 1st Mute, leading the coffin in a manner reminiscent of the early Funerary Violinists whose history he had so diligently preserved. He died in 1902, at the age of ninety-two.

Presidents of the Guild of Funerary Violinists 1804–1894

31. William Entwistle
President 1804–16

32. Joseph Burkham
President 1816–29

33. Charles Sudbury
President 1829–41

34. Matthew Connisten
President 1841–59

35. Adolphus Fullerton
President 1859–66

36. T. Yorick Prestbury
President 1866–74

37. Michael Elstridge
President 1874–81

38. Thomas Broadfoot
President 1881–87

39. Samson P. Wilton
President 1887–94

Paganini, the Vatican, and Rumours of Demonic Association

40. Etching of Paganini, after a painting by Maurin.

Though Paganini was never in any way connected with the tradition of Funerary Violin, his tremendous success and fame, combined with the intimations of devil worship and so forth that followed him across Europe were, as we have seen, to have a profound effect upon the genuine and worthy practitioners of the Art. In 1823 the chief magistrate of Dalmatia (Matthaus Nikolas de Ghetalde) was visiting Venice and heard rumours that the great Paganini was giving free open-air concerts every evening in the cemetery of the Venice Lido. This extract from a letter written to Peter Lichtenthal (his undersecretary, then back in Dalmatia) depicts the scene:

We went, and found a big crowd sitting and standing round, listening to Paganini play. Some people were amused and entertained, but most of them – with tears in their eyes – said it was so touching that this great artist played every evening, gratis, for the souls of the dead. [translated from the original Italian]

He goes on to describe how, on the way home, a Dominican monk in the gondola had told them that Paganini:

had sold his soul to the Devil and the Bishop had given orders not to allow him into the cemetery any more as he profaned that holy place. Our immediate and unanimous reaction was to pick the man up from his seat and throw him overboard, into the canal ...

The precise motive for this reaction is unclear: whether out of loyalty to Paganini, or sympathy for the audiences who couldn't possibly afford to see him at the opera house, or even a personal dislike of the Bishop we shall never know; however, this apparently innocuous event undoubtedly contributed to the growing backlash against, and ultimately wholesale destruction of, what was by then a flourishing art.

The unnamed monk complained personally to the Patriarch of Venice, Ján Krstitel Ladislav, a Hungarian ecclesiastic whose virulent piety deeply resented his own nation's love of music and, in particular, the violin, and who in turn took this complaint to Pope Pius VII himself.

As has already been seen in the chapter 'A Brief Summary of Early Funeral Music', the Church, and particularly the Roman Church, had always had a deep mistrust of music in any but its simplest forms. Christian thinkers had, of course, long been well aware of the potential dangers that lurk within the art of music. St Augustine, St Basil and St John Chrysostomus had all denounced 'these seductive sounds that so swiftly intoxicate the senses and weaken the soul'. For them, melodic instruments such as flutes and harps represented the 'Pomp of the Devil', and thus had no place in any form of righteous worship. The drum, an instrument made from the very skin of God's own creations, represented the death of the flesh itself. St Ambrose, always the moral pedant, and a man whose mistrust of gaiety extended even to a condemnation of laughter, specifically identifies the psaltery, gittern and drum with impiety and eternal death. He sharply criticises an offender:

While hymns are being recited, you are holding a gittern! While the psalms are being sung, you play on a psaltery or on a drum! This is truly outrageous, for in neglecting salvation you choose certain death!

St Bernard went so far as to declare that all musical instruments are 'not pleasing unto God', though he never elaborated on how he knew this to be the case.

The earliest Christians had sought to ban all forms of melodic music, believing that only the simplest of chants, devoid of ornament and vanity, would please the ear of God. For St Cyprian, 'the Lord hears not the voice but the heart', and St Jerome went still further in demanding that music should make no effort at aspiring towards beauty, insisting that 'command of beauty lies in the hands of God alone'; that 'the voice of Man is disharmonious by nature'; and even that 'the pure of heart have no eye for beauty, no ear for harmony, as these are merely vanities and the tools of the Devil'.

The Middle Ages saw a further condemnation of all forms of entertainment, and entertainers, both for social and spiritual reasons, considering, according to Alcuin, counsellor to Charlemagne, that those:

who offer up such froth and babble, who, through the ears and through the eyes inculcate vice into the spirit, are ministering to Satan himself alone.

Henri d'Autun, a twelfth-century cleric, added the rhetorical question:

May a minstrel expect to attain eternal life? Indeed not, for they are the ministers of the Devil.

Given this history, it is easy to see that the Catholic Church was deeply entrenched in a philosophy that mistrusted musicians, and feared the magical power of music to move people.

In addition, the French Revolution of 1789 had spread fear and paranoia amongst all the powerful institutions of Europe, the Roman Church included, and by the early 1820s Paganini's fame, wealth (he quickly became the best-paid musician in history, doubling the ticket prices at all the biggest opera houses and selling out days in a row) and extraordinary virtuosity was creating waves of envious rumours – most of which involved murder, time spent in prison and, more worryingly, an association with the devil. These rumours had already come to the attention of Pope Pius VII by 1822, and in 1823 he was heard by an anonymous young Cardinal to refer to Paganini as 'that most despicable of all Italians'. Though he was frequently denounced by the Church, this served but to further Paganini's fame, and therefore his success and wealth, and so Pope Pius's frustration only grew. His death late in 1823 created great politicking amongst the many Cardinals keen to take his place until the prefect of Rome, Annibale Francesco Clemente Melchiore Girolamo Nicola della Genga, was elected Pope Leo XII.

The new Pope continued Pius's fervent condemnation of all but the most austere of musical tastes, creating an anti-musical climate in the Vatican that was deeply entrenched by the time of his death in 1829. So it was a considerable shock to the Cardinals when they discovered that their new pontiff, Francesco Saverio Castiglioni, Pope Pius VIII, was not only a secret admirer of the violin but intended to employ a violinist to play to him as he went to sleep each night, claiming that the angelic music brought him close to God. Rumours abounded that his death, within the year, was not entirely a coincidence, and his successor, Bartolomeo Alberto (Mauro) Cappellari, Pope Gregory XVI, seized upon the ensuing paranoia as an excuse to embark on the Great Funerary Purges of the 1830s and 1840s. It is thought that Pope Gregory's extreme loathing of the violin was, in part if not entirely, due to his own blood relationship with the cause of all this trouble – the satanic Paganini (Paganini was a distant poor cousin of the Pope's own mother, Giulia Cesa-Pagani).

It is not known whether Pope Gregory was directly responsible for the purges that followed, or whether this was Cardinal Bartolomeo Pacca, but it is likely that the Pope had a quiet word with his favourite Cardinal. What we do know from the few historical records that were not either seized or burned is that the Great Funerary Purges lasted until 1846 (and the death of Pope Gregory), though they were at their peak around 1837–8.

Father Elias Passmore Jarvis

Feinatroprinol and the Myth of Spring-heeled Jack

41. Father Jarvis photographed c. 1870. This picture was kindly donated by the current Priest of St Mary's Church, Cubbington, Father Jonathan Walton, on the condition that it is made clear that any involvement Father Jarvis may have had with the Great Funerary Purges took place before his appointment to Cubbington, where he is known to have conducted himself with 'nothing but honour and integrity'.

There are, amongst the archives of the Guild of Funerary Violinists, a number of particularly tantalising documents, which, though they potentially cast considerable light on the dark period of the Great Funerary Purges, must nonetheless be treated with great caution, if not scepticism, as they have so far defied verification through any other sources. Amongst these, one of the most revealing, should it be true, is the *Testament of Fr Elias Passmore Jarvis*, written in 1883 and witnessed by Thomas Broadfoot, the then President of the Guild. How this Testament came to be written – whether Father Jarvis approached Broadfoot, or vice versa – is unknown, as no further references to the document have as yet been uncovered, but the general tone, and the age of Father Jarvis (given as in his seventy-eighth year), suggest that the motivation was guilt over his part in the events he describes,

42. Thomas Broadfoot c1882.

though he does deny this himself.

Father Jarvis spent much of his adult life as parish priest to St Mary's Church, Cubbington, but the Testament refers to his period as Deacon Forane for the Apostolic Vicariate of the London District during the late 1830s and early 1840s. This was a period of great change and increasing confidence for the English Catholic Church, following the Catholic Emancipation Act of 1829, which finally granted Catholics official equality (with some exceptions), and the consequent foundation of the Archdiocese of Westminster in 1850, amongst others. Although Father Jarvis gives us no names, the implications of what he says are palpably clear, and lay responsibility for the subsequent events firmly in the lap of the Roman hierarchy.

Were this account to stand entirely alone it might appear too fantastical to be given any credence whatever, but cross-referencing against contemporary newspaper articles and the records kept by Matthew Connisten on the many offences committed against the Guild and its members reveals, at the very least, a remarkable number of striking coincidences. The paper itself, and the ink, have been subjected to analysis, and verified as of the period, as has the handwriting, and so we can say, with some degree of certainty, that it could be genuine. This said, it is, of course, always a possibility that the whole account was fabricated by Thomas Broadfoot, with the intention of bringing into the open what he himself obviously believed to be true, as he would indeed have been one of the only people in possession of enough of the fa :ts to make such a fabrication. Until further evidence comes to light, therefore, tnis Testament can only be considered a tantalising clue as to what may have happened, and should be treated as no more than that.

Despite all these many uncertainties, the Testament is nonetheless, in the opinion of the author, a document of tremendous importance to the history of Funerary Violin, and I therefore present it here, in full:

I, Fr Elias Passmore Jarvis, on this, the 28th day of April, 1883, whilst in my 78th year, and still of sound mind, do solemnly declare that what I offer here is the Truth entire, and is offered of my own free will, without pressure or prejudice. Though I will not give the names of the many involved in the events I am to describe, for it is only for God to sit in judgement, I offer up this Testament that the Truth might at last be known, and my own frail heart might at last be cleansed of the doubt and guilt it has wrestled with for these many years.

Early in 1836, when I was still but a humble Deacon Forane in Westminster, a notable Cardinal arrived and had many long and secret discussions with my superior, Fr D—. Shortly after his visit I was, myself, summoned by Fr D— and entrusted with an important and secret mission. I was told that God himself was increasingly concerned about the heretical practices of Funerary Violinists, how they were conjuring the Devil in the very heartlands of England and Europe, and how immorality and mortal sin were being spread throughout the land in anticipation of the coming of the Antichrist. I was told that it was our duty to fight these demons, that the very Soul of Man was at stake, and that I had been gifted with a special role in these most Historic of times, in this, possibly the final battle between Good and Evil on the earth. I was told to seek out Soldiers of Christ amongst the poor and the destitute, the sinners and the depraved; I was told that the darker the heart, the sharper

*the sword in this, the most virtuous of all battles; I was told that the criminal
gangs of London's underworld should become my Legion of Christ, that I
should wage this war with all the subtlety and silence of a burglar in the night
as enemies were all around; and I was given gold, blessed by the Pope
himself, that would have the power to turn the heart from Avarice to Piety.
Certainly I was young, I was naïve, and such flattery induced in me so bold
a delusion of heroic grandiosity that I asked no questions, and set about my
task with much fervency and vigour.*

*I was, at the time, well known amongst the poor of Southwark and Westminster,
and not disrespected, and so it proved no great challenge to enlist my Soldiers
of the Underworld, not with gold in my purse. I preached and sermonised until
they understood the import of the task ahead; how we alone could save Mankind
from the coming of the Antichrist; how we held God's Kingdom in our hands;
and for every word I preached, the glitter of the gold preached two.*

*Fr D— then instructed me in the first details of my mission; we must seize
all artefacts referring to the tradition of Funerary Violin; we must destroy
the very foundations of the tradition; we must undo its very history; we must
leave no memory for sinners of the future to look back on; we must cast the
net of Christ around each thought or whisper that refers to it, and drag them
back into the sight of the Lord. I was also given a large bottle of special holy
water, from the spring at Nazareth, and blessed by the Pope himself. This, I
was told, was not for me, but for the Soldiers of Christ, and was only to be
drunk directly before entering the lair of Satan himself. I understood and set
about my task with much fervency and vigour.*

*Before long the results of my work were becoming evident, a stream of books,
documents, letters and journals from private libraries, and even occasionally violins were coming through my hands to Fr D—, and, I believe, were
secretly shipped on to Rome; each item paid for in gold and holy water. My
soldiers were keen in their art of destruction, buildings associated with the
Evil were burned, Funerary Violinists were injured in 'random street robberies', leaving them alive but unable to play. All in the name of Christ. All
in the name of the Lord. And I soon noticed what I believed to be a change
in the spirit of my flock; before long their enthusiasm for the holy water was
becoming greater than their love of gold. At first I took this for religious
fervour, believing my mission to be divinely ordained, but soon this fervour
turned to aggression. Their desperation for the water seemed to be turning*

them insane with desire for God's presence. Perplexed, and not a little afeared I asked Fr D— for guidance and he revealed something entirely unexpected.

He revealed that this was not merely water, but a recipe dictated by God to F— R— to be used in our battle with this most dire of Evils. He said it gives great strength and spiritual veracity for the battles ahead, though if taken with too great a frequency it can cause delusions and ultimately madness. No mortal man can stare into the face of God for long and retain his sanity, he said. It was not my concern. I must continue with my work. I understood and set about my task with much fervency and vigour.

Then, in September 1837, the newspapers started talking of Spring-heeled Jack. At first I took this as a sign of the coming of the Antichrist, as his appearances seemed to occur in the areas where my Soldiers of Christ were in action. We were winning, I thought; we were driving the Devil himself out into the open. There could be no other explanation. But then, as my soldiers returned with their spoils of war, their appearance would sometimes be wild, bestial, their movements exaggerated and effortless, their eyes bright red as if on fire, their desperation for the water, or 'red mist' as they called it, driving them ever onwards. Once again I turned to Fr D— for guidance. He said it was all part of the Good Lord's plan; what better disguise for the Soldiers of Christ, than the visage of the Devil, he said; and seeing them, the people would be made aware of the Devil's presence and repent, he said; it was not my concern. I must continue with my work. But my questions had surely become his concern for shortly thereafter I was sent to Cubbington to become a curate and I never again heard of this holy battle, being told it was not any longer for me to be aware of these things; I had served my Lord in this mission and must now content myself with preaching the gospel to good Catholics.

And so I did for nigh on forty years, but now, with the clarity of age and wisdom I am at last free to question these events, and, though I cannot say I know the Truth, though I cannot be certain that the battle was real or false, though I am no longer even sure whose fight this really was, I know that I did play a part, that the Antichrist was held at bay, and that it is right to lay down this Testimony that others might judge these things for themselves in the future. I do not apologise to the Guild of Funerary Violinists, who have asked me to commit this history to paper; I do not seek forgiveness from those who even now perpetuate much subtle Evil in this world; I merely wish to put the record straight as to what I have done in my life, that I might soon greet God with my conscience clear.

The final statement adds further ambiguity to the motivation behind the Testament, and the final dig at the Guild clearly demonstrates that, though he may have questioned whether his actions were true to God, his sympathies had not changed, and his view of the Guild and its activities remained unaltered. Though I am disinclined to comment further on the credibility of this account, there are a number of points worthy of clarification, most notably the reference to 'Spring-heeled Jack'.

The first reported sightings occurred in September of 1837 around Barnes Common in south-west London. A businessman was returning home from work late at night when a mysterious figure vaulted over the railings of a cemetery. The railings were at least 10 feet high, but the creature effortlessly leaped over the wall and landed directly in the path of the man. He was described as having pointed ears, large glowing eyes, and a large pointed nose. Thereafter sightings were reported frequently, each involving very similar acrobatic antics, and each description including fiery red eyes. He soon became something of a folk villain and was quickly appropriated for fictional entertainment: the first play, *Spring-Heeled Jack, The Terror of London* by John Thomas Haines, being produced as early as 1840. In many of the recorded accounts of his appearance, the days and locations tally with Matthew Connisten's records for robberies and arson attacks against the Guild and its members. Therefore it is not impossible that Spring-heeled Jack and Jarvis's Soldiers of Christ were one and the same.

Another point that has been the cause of much discussion and debate over the years is the actual nature of the holy water, or 'red mist', mentioned by Father Jarvis. Current research has concluded that the most likely candidate is fienatroprinol, a suspension of caffeine and atropine (a distillation from *Atropa belladonna*) in alcohol. First derived by Friedrich Ferdinand Runge, an analytical chemist based in Vienna, in 1833, fienatroprinol was an early, and dangerous, form of physical and psychotic stimulant, the most visible side effect of which is an intense redness of the eyes caused by the opposing effects of the caffeine and atropine attempting to dilate and contract the pupil simultaneously. It is also known to cause a considerable increase in heart rate, energy, motivation, and feelings of well-being, and in larger quantities can undermine the awareness of pain. It proved to be highly addictive, and long-term use often resulted in blindness followed by heart failure.

It was banned in England in 1877 after a number of deaths in the middle-class communities in London (addicts had been dying unnoticed in the London slums for many years), and thereafter sightings of Spring-heeled Jack first decreased and then stopped altogether.

43. The first page of Father Jarvis's Testament, written in his own difficult and spidery hand. The final page bears the signatures of both Father Jarvis and Thomas Broadfoot, the then President of the Guild of Funerary Violinists.

Wilhelm Kleinbach

The last of the practising Funerary Violinists

44. Wilhelm Kleinbach c. 1870.

Born in 1830, in the outskirts of Vienna, to a family of cabinet makers, Wilhelm Kleinbach was to be the last of the notable Funerary Violinists. A grand-student of Herr Gratchenfleiss himself, he had taken up the profession just as the Great Funerary Purges of the Catholic Church were destroying it, and continued the practice in secret into the early twentieth century, through an underground network of dedicated followers of the art. Often performing in the dead of night at Vienna's

Zentralfriedhof, before a select gathering of cognoscenti assembled to hear his performance, who often hadn't known the deceased, Kleinbach developed an international reputation amongst the handful of individuals still taking an interest in this most mortal of art forms. Scholarship has revealed very few specific details about his life, but some accounts of these moonlit vigils, performing the works of Herr Gratchenfleiss to the dead, have survived.

Wilhelm Kleinbach was a student of Thomas Techler, who was, in turn, Gratchen-fleiss's favourite, making Kleinbach a direct link to the great masters of Funerary Violin. Though entirely forgotten for many years after his death, his position in history was forever assured thanks to a series of wax cylinders he recorded at the very end of his life. That these recordings exist at all is something of a miracle, given that they are the result of a fortunate coincidence. Karl Weinfurter, a young gentleman of leisure who lived two doors down from Kleinbach, in a middle-class suburb of Hamburg (to which Kleinbach had moved after an unfortunate incident during one of his performances, which resulted in his expulsion from Vienna in 1881), acquired an acoustic recording device that used wax cylinders (and later a system for transfer to 78 r.p.m. discs) and, upon hearing Kleinbach practising, suggested that he might use him to test out his new equipment. It can be heard from the recordings that he did many experiments with different acoustics, and sizes and materials for the horn, with mixed results. The recordings were made between 1906 and 1911 (judging by the original cylinders), when Kleinbach was in his late seventies and early eighties. Though the intonation is at times a little shaky, the power and intensity of his playing is clearly still evident.

It was not until 1990, seven years after the discovery of the Hildesheim trunk, that scholars identified these previously unknown pieces (located in the music library of the Hamburg Institute for Social Research) as the works of Herr Gratchenfleiss. So far fifteen of the pieces have been deciphered from the rotting pages of the notebooks, and twelve of Kleinbach's recordings match these works. In some cases his recordings are different from the written versions, with changes in structure and octave, and occasional variations – possibly due to his deteriorating technique, or the constraints of working to a two- or four-minute wax cylinder. Given the notebooks' current state of preservation, it is impossible to say how many more works will be uncovered before their complete disintegration. There are another twenty cylinders and four discs in the collection that do not correspond to any known works at present. The entire collection was recently acquired by the Guild of Funerary Violinists, and is currently being subjected to further study.

The Collection of Gunter II

and his Unusually Long Wax Cylinders

45. Prince Gunter II c. 1905.

In 1910 Gunter II, Prince of Schwarzburg-Rudolstadt-Sonderhausen, commis-sioned, from Thomas Edison's company, an extraordinarily long Dictaphone machine and a set of thirty blank wax cylinders of a full 12 inches. This was, at the time, the only recording machine capable of recording up to ten minutes of continuous music or words, and remains a unique object to this day. It is currently owned by the Guild of Funerary Violinists who, it is alleged, acquired it in the chaos following the Second World War.

Gunter II was, even by German standards, a profound eccentric, who was driven by two major obsessions: military prowess, and his passion for collecting objects of funerary furniture. Amongst his extensive collection there were said to be the coffins of Goethe and Heine, the death mask of Beethoven, the last will and testament of Napoleon Bonaparte, a cranial mould of Sir Isaac Newton and many other objects of apparent renown. He was also notable for being the last aristocratic gentleman in Europe to privately employ an official Funerary Violinist at his court: a post that he created in 1901 and that was filled by Niklaus Friedhaber until Gunter II's death in 1915.

It is not known how he came to hear of the Guild of Funerary Violinists as it had, at this time, been operating underground since the tragic fire at its central offices during the Great Funerary Purges in 1841, but in 1901 Gunter II made it known, through an agent, that he would pay well for any relics or papers that referred to it, or could be shown to be involved with its history. It is this collection, amongst a few others, that forms the backbone of the archives of the Guild as it slowly pieces together its history after considerable destruction and persecution over the years.

Although much of the archives remains, as yet, uncatalogued, because of the extensive cross-referencing involved, and the stripping away of the many myths that have arisen over the years, the Guild has been focusing particularly on Gunter II's collection of wax cylinders, recorded between 1910 and 1914. These are incredibly fragile, because of their unique length of 12 inches (with a 3-inch diameter), and the transfer process is slow as the cylinders themselves must be completely reinforced and copper-coated before playing. There are twenty-five in all, and the seven we have so far transferred include a performance of Thomas Dinsley's recreation of Babcotte's *Erroneous Dirge*, and a number of pieces from Charles Sudbury's *Funerary Suite no. 4.*

Gunter II, like any cultured gentleman of the time, was a perfectly good violinist, and his labels imply that he himself was the performer on these cylinders, but current study suggests that this is unlikely as the styles and techniques vary across the recordings and they are clearly not all by the same player. It has been speculated that he may be the player on a few of the recordings (including the Babcotte Dirge) in which the performance style is more classical and cultured, but equally, if he is known to have misrepresented the artist in some recordings, can we believe he was honest in others?

We are given no clues as to the actual identity of the players involved, nor whether they were Funerary Violinists or merely concert artists. The current opinion of the Guild is, however, that a number of the Sudbury recordings are by a formally trained Funerary Violinist, as the spirit and colour seem too true to the genre to be mere imitation. Although it is likely that at least some of the recordings were performed by Friedhaber, many scholars have suggested that the style bears a remarkable resemblance to the playing on Wilhelm Kleinbach's recordings of the works of Herr Gratchenfleiss, who was by then in his early eighties, as the performance style, technical inaccuracies, variable tuning and casual deviations from the score have much in common with those now famous recordings. In addition, the Sudbury recordings are punctuated by much gratuitous, obscene and largely incomprehensible cursing on the part of the performer.

Stanley Eaton

From Potential Genius to Undertaker

46. Stanley Eaton c. 1913, around the
time of his visit to Prince Gunter II.

Stanley Eaton, the last great hope of the Guild of Funerary Violinists, was born in
1885, in London. His father, Thomas Eaton, had been a Guild member since 1876,
and though not a practising Funerary Violinist, was much involved in the admini-
stration of the Guild (a difficult task in those secretive times) and teaching the

works and aesthetic to the younger generation, so it is no great surprise that his eldest son was to become his prize student.

Stanley showed great flair for the violin from the age of six, and by twelve he is known to have given private recitals at secret Guild events. When he was fourteen he successfully auditioned for the Royal Academy of Music, and received a scholarship to study under Sir Richard Ardsley. It was this exposure to serious concert music that was to create a conflict in him that was only resolved thirteen years later with the composition of his *Great Funerary Sonata* (as it is now known).

Having tasted the depth and scale of the classical masterworks, he was reluctant to return to the more tightly constrained and rigorously focused repertoire of Funerary Violin. But at the same time, his love of the sombre coquetry of the Funerary Aesthetic was deeply entrenched, and so he resolved to draw the two together through the creation of a new repertoire of works, true to the spirit of both traditions, and thus bring the Funerary Aesthetic into the concert hall. After much study and several false starts, he finally took the first steps of this potentially most epic of musical journeys, with the composition of his Funerary Sonata no.1, by far the largest-scale work of Funerary Violin ever composed, consisting of three immense movements (loosely speaking a March, a Dream and a Panic) and lasting a full twenty-five minutes.

Tragically, this was the only substantial work he was to complete, as he was called up a year later to serve in the trenches of the First World War, and lost his right arm in 1916 in an unexplained incident of friendly fire. After the war he emigrated to America and, after a number of years in penury, qualified as a funeral director in 1926. His family business did not offer music as part of its service.

Stanley Eaton is thought to have stayed with Gunter II in December 1913, and made a recording of his *Great Funerary Sonata* during this stay; a recording is currently preserved in the archives of the Guild. Eaton was obsessed with depth and penetration of tone, and was lucky enough to have been loaned a Guanerius Del Gesu violin, unthinned by repairers, and therefore strong enough to tune a whole tone higher than standard pitch. This recording clearly demonstrates the brightness achieved by such a tuning, as it does his intense vibrato. In addition, he has stood further from the recording horn than was conventional, and as a result you can hear the echo of his powerful instrument bouncing around the room, an effect most unusual at the time, and one of the first examples of reverb being deliberately cultivated in a recording.

47. Stanley Eaton's diploma from the Syracuse School of Embalming, from which he graduated in 1926. His family business continued successfully after his death in 1963, until 1986, when it finally closed after the death of his son, Albert.

The Great Funerary Sonata

Undoubtedly Eaton's most important contribution to the Art was his *Great Funerary Sonata* of 1912: a work of unparalleled proportions in the entire history of Funerary Violin, which can be viewed as a final reconciliation to its own dissolution in the face of the then burgeoning concert music tradition. Indeed, it is as if the Art of Funerary Violin were being laid at the feet of the classical tradition saying: 'Here is my soul: do with it as you will.'

Composed in three movements, it does contain many of the elements constituent to the nineteenth-century Funerary Suite, but re-envisaged with concert hall aspirations. The simple strophic and ternary forms favoured in the Funerary Suites are replaced by a large-scale classical arching of the kind much favoured by later twentieth-century composers such as Bartók, imposing a self-conscious emotional evolution upon the movements akin to the classical sonata form. It was this same emotional evolution that Herr Gratchenfleiss had banished from the Art on the grounds that:

> *by the time of death the Soul has already grown to its final fruition; there is therefore no profit to be gained by shallow imitations of our mortal conflicts and the many debates between head and heart that so inform the music of those fashionable entertainers who court the favours of the wealthy and the worldly ...*   (*Herr Hieronymous Gratchenfleiss*)
> [translated from the original German]

However, this departure from what some saw as the very essence of the tradition is both understandable and justifiable, given the period of composition. It should be remembered that by 1912 it was nearly sixty years since the last officially sanctioned performance in Britain by a Funerary Violinist at a funeral, and very few members of the Guild could recall the days when it was a common practice. It had become a tradition without a function – a secretive, even paranoid association of amateur musicians whose love of the genre was governed entirely by private concerts and a certain conspiratorial one-upmanship. Stanley Eaton, who had grown up with this music, wanted to bring it once again to the ears of the public, and by the early twentieth century the only way to do this was through concerts.

This was a period when concert violinists were the pop stars of their day; Ysaÿe, Enescu, Sarasate and Kreisler were thrilling audiences all over the world, and Eaton, a fine virtuoso himself, recognised that if he took the Funerary Aesthetic into the concert hall he could possibly inspire a popular restoration of the tradition to its rightful place at the graveside. But to do that he had to disguise it as concert music, and create a grand work that might stand its ground in a programme next to Beethoven, Mozart or Brahms.

Given such sincere intentions in his composing of the *Great Funerary Sonata*, we should surely forgive him its many inadequacies in representing the Funerary Aesthetic, and indeed, it was intended merely as a first step: were it not for the tragic loss of his right arm only three years later, and his subsequent disillusionment with music, who knows what other masterful works might have flowed from his pen, bringing him ever closer to the pure expression of that which he so desired to impart.

The first movement, entitled 'Knocking at the Door' and bearing the marking *moderato grandioso,* encompasses many of the symbolic elements of the more traditional march movements of the Funerary Suite. Its bold repetitions; its considerable use of the open G-string in imitation of a bass drum; its insistent use of the rhythm

as a motto symbolic of Death knocking at the door; its reliance upon shifting drones and semi-modal harmonies to inject an impression of movement: all these are true to the original vision of Herr Gratchenfleiss. However, they are all treated with much greater flexibility than in the earlier funerary works, functioning more as a general rule than as specific guidelines. It is the emotional argument of the piece that makes it stand outside the tradition.

In effect there are four distinct sections, each with its own distinct emotional tone. The first section sees Death come knocking at the door; the Soul is reluctant and Death uses all its powers of seduction in its attempt to persuade the Soul away from mortal existence. The second section depicts the struggle as the Soul and Death fight for possession of the body; the third section depicts the resignation of the Soul as it reluctantly takes Death by the hand; and the fourth section depicts the triumph of Death (a popular subject in the traditional Funerary Suite). None of these is unfamiliar territory for the Funerary Violinist, but the placing of them together into one emotional journey, and particularly the use of transition sections, was an entirely bold, unconventional and potentially dangerous step at the time, making it an entirely new kind of funerary piece.

The second movement, entitled 'Introduction to the Angels' and bearing the marking *moderato espressivo,* is more traditional in many ways, although its emotional arch is still far greater than would have been considered appropriate at the time, laying it open to accusations of self-indulgence. In form it is something of a cross between the traditional Dream and Flight, depicting the Soul's first tentative steps towards freedom from mortal bonds: a moment of euphoria before the lost dark Spirits that seek the stain of mortal sin have gathered and judgement can commence. This movement is open and airy as would be expected, and makes considerable use of consecutive fifths, an interval symbolically associated with the cleansing of the Soul in the traditional Funerary Suite.

The final movement, entitled 'The Purging of Mortal Sin' and bearing the marking *lento – allegro con moto – lento,* is again a combination of two traditional elements of the Funerary Suite, the Eulogy and the Panic – taking the tripartite form of an introduction (Eulogy); the main body of the movement (Panic), which is repeated; and a final postlude that virtually repeats the opening Eulogy. The introduction itself refers to the works of Pierre Dubuisson in its use of major/minor alternation and simple open-string double stops, and successfully presents an air of sadness and resignation without tragedy. It is in the main body of this movement that we see Eaton at his most passionate and original. Although it is very much in the traditional spirit of a Panic, he has brought many more modern vituoso elements into the performance (such as left-hand pizzicato, and considerable use of folkish ornamentation), whilst maintaining and even extending the deep sense of alarm and panic desired in the form. In addition, it encompasses much of the traditional symbolism of the Funerary Violinist: for example, sudden jarring time-signature changes; considerable use of open fifths; shifting drones and modal harmony; use of the open G in imitation of a drum. It can be seen as something of a compendium of Funerary Violinistic techniques, and is in many ways a fitting conclusion to the once great tradition as it finally dissolved, even as an intention, amidst the guns of the First World War, when death became common place and all funerary aggrandisements were finally cast aside as we entered the modern world: a world in which Funerary Violin is, for many, no longer even a distant memory.

48. A page from the original score of the final movement of Eaton's *Great Funerary Sonata*.

The Funerary Violinist Today

Not infrequently people have asked me what is the relevance of Funerary Violin to them. Other than the obvious send-off it can offer, they seem to see no link between the many issues and burdens that trouble their everyday lives and the Art of Funerary Violin. But they could not be more mistaken. If only they would take a few minutes to contemplate the profound lessons that can be learnt from the Art, they would see that the ramifications reach out way beyond the chapel of rest, beyond art and culture itself, and into our general relationship with the world, mortality and our responses to them. Just as an archaeologist can perceive many elements of a long lost civilisation from a single damaged artefact, or an ecologist can judge the health of an entire ecosystem from a single lichen, just so the thoughtful and far-sighted amongst us can judge the spiritual and material values of our own culture through the status and social depiction of the Funerary Violinist. The current poor health of what was once a great tradition is testament to the declining vision, or – dare I say it – selective wilful blindness, of the society we express through our everyday lives.

Certainly the thread of continuity was broken by the Great Funerary Purges, but today, in the light of all that has been discovered in recent years, and that is indeed presented herein, it is no longer possible to plead simple ignorance. Despite incredible efforts on the part of the Guild of Funerary Violinists, and others, in recent years, it is apparent that our culture has turned its back on the serious and meaningful; death itself has become taboo, and our hopes for a renaissance of our venerable Art, now long overdue, are to be thwarted by the overwhelming indifference of a media-dominated material consumer world.

But we look to the future, and we know that such a state of affairs cannot possibly last, for funerary rites are an eternal feature of man's psychological make-up. They are amongst the oldest known rituals. Even in the days before artefacts that might now suggest to the imaginative scholar any number of bold speculations as to the spiritual world of ancient peoples, the earliest of modern humans are known to have sprinkled their dead with red ochre – a natural orangey pigment. This is taken to be amongst the first signs of the spiritual consciousness that allegedly sets us apart from the animals. Indeed, as we have seen, much of our understanding of history is drawn from the leftovers of complex funerary rituals – such as the Sutton Hoo ship burial, the pyramids of Egypt, and so forth. Our knowledge of many early civilisations is limited entirely to what can be gleaned from their grave goods, and the implications therein. In the present day we see a bewildering array of funerary rites around the world, from marathon prayer session, to the burning of massive pyres. Yet when we look to our own modern western culture we see little more than a basic rejection of the notion of death.

Today we are, as a society, convinced that modern medicine will prolong life to the point where it is no longer worth the effort. Of course, this point to a man or woman in their twenties looks very different from how it looks to a person of seventy-five, but the reassuring smile of medical science means that only the tragically unfortunate must ever contemplate the reality of death whilst in their prime. Once the body is near to breaking down for good, they are sent away to a nursing home that deals with everything at a distance. Most of us have never seen a dead body. If there is a death in the family, it is usually that of an elderly relative whom we last saw some time ago. The brief funeral is led by somebody who never met the deceased, and it is not uncommon for mistakes to be made in summarising the life. The body is safely packaged in a standard off-the-shelf coffin and, more often than not nowadays, this coffin puts in only a brief appearance before being mechanically retracted behind curtains. All this to the plaintive strains of a cassette player churning out commercially motivated music. Upon occasion, an electric organ is played (badly) by another stranger to the deceased. A week or so later the family are presented with an elegant wooden box, or urn, containing the unrecognisable ashes, which are usually sprinkled somewhere pretty. If there is a burial, a simple headstone will suffice, or a small plaque embedded in the ground, but to celebrate the death with a grand mausoleum would be considered tasteless. Of course, there are a number of specialist trades that deal with the dead on our behalf, such as hospital workers, mortuary attendants and undertakers, but they are the exception to the rule.

This whole process has evolved over the last eighty or so years, to distance us from any uncomfortable notions of our own mortality. In a world where animal products come processed and packaged from the supermarket, where plastic surgery can keep us looking young (though a little strange) well into our seventies, and where our apparent gods are celebrated for the enviableness of their lifestyles, it is no great surprise that mortality is placed at the very back of our minds. And in this current state of denial anything that focuses the attention on the reality of our great journey through life will inevitably be rejected. Such has been the recent fate of the once great Art of Funerary Violin.

If you take a walk through any British nineteenth-century cemetery, such as Highgate (London) or Woodvale (Brighton), you will see a wonderful array of gothic sculptures, grand mausolea, and crumbling stones overgrown with bushes and brambles – a remnant from the days when Romantic Gothicism was deemed an appropriate response to death. What more fitting place, you may think, for a Funerary Violinist to rehearse the tone that is the mark of his trade – but according to Southwark Council, by-law 3, article 7.2 (amongst others), you would be wrong. Not only has cultural evolution turned its back on the Art of Funerary Violin, but individual councils have enacted specific laws to prevent the prospective Funerary Violinist from learning his art.

Some may consider rehearsing in cemeteries unnecessary, but to them I say: could a Formula One driver practise his skills along winding country lanes? could a cross-channel swimmer train in a local swimming pool? Of course they could, but it would only be useful up to a point. The final element is missing, and without it their training is inevitably limited. Just so with the Funerary Violinist. Performing at a funeral, venerating the dead, becoming a vehicle for the grief of many is not just another concert. It has a quality all of its own, and without the proper rehearsal environment this cannot be achieved. Ask yourself – would you like an unrehearsed violinist to play at the funeral of one of your loved ones? I think not!

Let us consider for a minute what a Funerary Violinist actually does: the key to this is sensitivity. The chapel of rest is filled with strangers, all in a highly emotional and sometimes desperate state; the coffin containing their loved one is laid out at the front. Whilst everyone is still stirring, the violinist takes up his bow (I say 'his', as traditionally Funerary Violinists were all male, though the Guild is now hesitantly encouraging membership from woman, albeit Honorary and not Executive) and begins the ritual. This moment is crucial, and if misjudged can lead to disaster.

In his tone he must first convey the deep grief that is present in the room and then transform it into a thing of beauty. By the time he is finished, a deep and plaintive calm should have descended upon the room, and the bereaved should be ready to hear the eulogy. The music must be simple; any hint of flashiness or empty virtuosity, even the slightest breath of ego, will destroy the spell. At the end of the ceremony the Funerary Violinist must again strike up and take the mourners back to the world of sadness and grief for the weeping at the graveside (or in the car park, if the body was cremated).

This is music as magic, with the ability to transform the mood and perceptions of the audience in a way far beyond what is possible in the concert hall – and it only works on such a deep level because the audience is in a heightened emotional state. The Funerary Violinist's position is one of great responsibility and it should not be taken lightly. Sadly, it is a profound reflection on our current culture that more often than not the default choice at a funeral is an electric organ playing something nondescript, or a pre-recorded cassette. I believe this is a response to our fear of the power of meaningful rituals – and, again, our love of plastic packaging.

In many ways the Funerary Violinist is the last bastion of Romanticism. In a world where 'art' refers to all things so long as they are in an art gallery, and where John Cage has demonstrated that all sound in a concert hall is music, the Funerary Violinist remains un-redefined. It is a role that defies reinvention, because it deals with an absolute. Death remains death whatever we call it, however much we distance ourselves from it, and just so with Funerary Violin. It is the channel for the expression of death, and as such can only be what it is. To stray too far from the truth is to fail. In today's world the Funerary Violinist is the lone Romantic who dares to stand on the peak and look down into the black chasm beyond, whilst everyone else cowers in the foothills admiring designer shoes in shop windows. As a civilised culture we cannot afford to let this ancient and venerable tradition, which dates back over 400 years, remain forgotten; we cannot afford to ignore the many valuable lessons it holds for us; and most of all, we cannot afford to push death and mortality ever further from our minds, for that way lies only madness.

Epilogue: A Response from the Vatican

After many years spent piecing together this forgotten history, and having compiled from a great many sources what I felt was a convincing, if not comprehensive, picture of the final destruction and dismantling of the form during the Great Funerary Purges, it seems incontrovertible that the Catholic Church was, if not entirely, at least largely responsible for the venerable tradition's demise. In the interests of objectivity, sound journalism and historical fair play, I felt it my duty to present these findings to the Vatican itself, in the hope that maybe, in these more tolerant times, they might take the opportunity to open up their archives and finally lay to rest some of the many questions that are raised in this book. I therefore put together a thorough report of all the evidence I had acquired that pointed the finger of suspicion in their direction – from the detailed accounts of Matthew Connisten of crimes committed against the Guild, to the confession of Father Jarvis (and a number of other documents too contentious to be mentioned here) – and posted it to Monseigneur Georg Ganswein, Pope Benedict XVI's private secretary. It was a number of months before I received an answer, from the Holy See Press Office, and again in the interests balance and objectivity, I include their response here, in full:

Dear Mr Kriwaczek,
 The accusations you, and others, are making, are clearly preposterous, and, were it not for the serious and libellous nature of your plainly misguided allegations, we would not deem them worthy of an answer.

Pope Gregory XVI was a profoundly pious and peaceful man, who commissioned the composition of many masses, and your suggestion that he had an abhorrence of music has no basis in fact. The allegation that his mother was related to Paganini is again entirely unfounded. We can see no evidence amongst what you have sent that the Catholic Church had anything whatever to do with what you call 'The Great Funerary Purges', and would strongly question whether such a series of events even occurred; and your many slanderous accusations against Cardinal Bartolomeo Pacca are absurd, as he is known to have never left Italy during his lifetime. We have no records whatever of Father Elias Passmore Jarvis, and would suggest that his alleged confession is nothing more than a crude forgery.

Though we cannot imagine why you have gone to so much trouble in fabricating this evident string of lies and slanders, we would advise you to be very careful in considering whether or not to publish this absurd and libellous concoction you choose to call a book, as the consequences for you, and those who support you in this venture, may be disastrous. Do not forget that the Good Lord sides with Righteous.

We can only assume that either this is some form of a sick practical joke, or that you, and those you are working with, are suffering from severe mental health issues.

We hope that this response will give you cause to reconsider your actions and how you choose to proceed.

In all good Faith,

George Resnik
For and on behalf of the Press Office of the Holy See

Reading a little between the lines, it was clear to me that the defensive and mildly threatening tone of this response indicated that my assumption must be correct, and that the Vatican archives did indeed hold the key to the truth behind the Great Funerary Purges. Spurred on by what I took to be a positive outcome, I sent a second, more detailed account of my findings, taking particular care to address the few specific issues that their letter had denied. Again, it took nearly two months for a reply to be forthcoming, and it is here quoted in full:

Dear Mr Kriwaczek,

We regret to say that you must be mistaken. We have no record of any previous contact from you, nor of the report that you claim to have sent. There has never been a George Resnik employed by this office, and the 'mildly threatening' language that you claim was used by the said George Resnik would be wholly inappropriate and incompatible with an office representing His Holiness Pope Benedict XVI. We therefore categorically deny having anything to do with it.

In short, we have no idea what on earth you are talking about.

Sincerely and in all good Faith,

Robert E. Lamplue
For and on behalf of the Press Office of the Holy See

This second response, and particularly its denial of the previous letter, despite the many consistencies between the two (such as the identical headed paper they were printed on, and the sign off 'in all good Faith' with a capital F) made it even clearer to me that I was on the right track. That they had completely ignored all of the specific evidence and references included in my own second letter only added to this conviction.

Not wishing to let the matter lie so easily, I gathered together copies of all the evidence I had presented in my previous two correspondences and sent them, this time, directly to Pope Benedict XVI himself, together with a copy of the previous two responses. That was nearly a year ago and I have, as yet, received no written reply; however, a number of unexplained and disturbing instances have occurred since then. Although individually they may be seen as unconnected, when put together they bear a remarkable and profound resemblance to the Great Funerary Purges themselves.

On 15 July 2004 there was a fire at the offices of the Guild of Funerary Violinists, then based in Highbury, London, in which the lower two floors were entirely destroyed. Thankfully nobody was hurt and most of the Guild's archives had already been moved to various institutions pending further detailed study. An investigation concluded that it was the result of arson, but the culprits were never found. Since then there have been a number of other occurrences, which I am unable to report at present (as they are still under investigation by the police), save to say that I have the impression that my own life may well be in danger. Despite this, I do not regret my actions, as the search for truth, however hard it may become, is what sets man apart, and certainly I will not be the first to have suffered such indignities and threats in the name of the Art of Funerary Violin. Let us only hope that I am not the last.

A Brief Tribute to the Many Silent Heroes

An Acknowledgement of Those Who Carried the Torch During the Darkest of Times

There are, of course, in all histories, a great many people whose exploits are too trivial, or whose achievements too small, to be worthy of inclusion, but without whom, nonetheless, many details might have been very different, many stories lost, and many pages in the book of time left unwritten. And so it is with this incomplete history. After the Great Funerary Purges, and the instigation of the 'New and Secretive Way' under the leadership of Matthew Connisten, the Guild turned its efforts to the preservation of its Art and traditions: gathering from across Europe the scattered remnants of its once great corpus of music, philosophy and spiritual consideration; drawing together evidence of the many stories that make up its history, which, until its destruction, had been so taken for granted that none had paid them much concern; and consolidating what it had once been, that some day an account might be presented to the world of what was lost. And although I am obliged to say nothing of the manner of their many great efforts and achievements, nor of the various difficulties they faced in execution of this self-imposed task, I must acknowledge that without their labours and tireless scholarship my own life would have been very different, this book could not have been written, and the world would be without a great and noble Art, which, though currently unvalued and largely unknown, may well one day be called upon to once again take up the torch and light the bridge between this world and the next.

The following pages can therefore be seen as something of a roll-call of honour for those many silent workers whose individual contributions may have been slight, but when put together constitute the very survival of the Art to this day. (Regrettably, I am unable to acknowledge any whose efforts were made after 1918, other than to thank them in general, and to hope that one day the climate will be such that all obligations to secrecy are finally deemed to be no longer of any relevance.)

49. P. Quivercheek

50. M. E. Tromans

51. D. Francolini

52. T. Sagar

53. L. N. Gould

54. P. J. Dickinson

55. S. Stanzeleit

56. M. Hamilton

57. D. Y. Breuer

58. T. N. Burlington

59. J. Bixby

60. G. Landver

The Governing Board of the Guild of Funerary Violinists 1897

61. Thomas Syddall
Secretary

62. Donald J. Whichell

63. James Sutherland
President 1894–1907

64. John Pocock

65. Charles Eveleigh

Appendix I

Records of the Spread of Funerary Violin by Babcotte's Apprentices

In the interest of brevity, and given that there is no further information on any of these individuals, I present the following list as an indication of the sudden spread of Babcotte's art into Catholic Europe during the seventeenth century, by what can only have been his Catholic apprentices.

In 1608 Benedict le Bone is recorded as in the employ of Christian Günther, Count of Schwarzburg-Sonderhausen, as Funerary Violinist and, in 1615, Master of the Count's Funerary Violinists, indicating that by 1615 the Count had a number of such artists in his employ.

In 1608 William Ruggwain is recorded as holding the post of Funerary Violinist at the court of Henry IV of France, and continued in that position under Louis XIII until his death in 1623.

In 1609 Ambrose Wyghtham is employed as Funerary Violinist to George Frederick, Margrave of Baden-Durlach – a post he holds until 1619, when his name is no longer recorded.

By 1611 (and possibly earlier) Roger Flexney is employed as Funerary Violinist by John George, Count of Hohenzollern-Hechingen. There are no further references to him and so the duration of his tenure is unknown.

Appendix II

The Tragic Miscalculation of Maria Rotaru

66. This photograph of Maria Rotaru c. 1975 was printed on the back of the ill-fated Melodiya recording. A victim of Soviet repression, she was expunged from almost all records during the late 1970s, making this image, and the accompanying recording, the only remaining evidence of her tragically short life.

In 1975, third-bench violinist and failed composer Maria Rotaru attempted to kick-start her career by passing off the Babcotte Dirge as her own work. How she came by a copy is unknown, but her attempt at plagiarism suggests she was well aware that the work was entirely unknown, at least in the Eastern bloc.

At first the Romanian musical establishment was greatly impressed by this substantial new work for solo violin, and even arranged for a recording to be made (which was to be released on Melodiya). However, shortly after the initial imprint

was produced, the piece was denounced in *Scînteia* – Romania's official Commu-
nist Party newspaper – not as a fraud, but as Formalistic, probably on the order of
Ceausescu himself, and Rotaru disappeared on 18 September 1975. Only fifty
copies were ever printed, and it wasn't until 1992, after the collapse of the Soviet
Union, that the piece was correctly identified as the *Erroneous Dirge*. Since then,
copies of this recording have become collectors' items and have reached over
£1,500 at auction (Sotheby's, 28 February 2005).

Appendix III

The Judicious Use of a Drum?

It is impossible to say with any degree of certainty when a bass drum was first used to accompany the performance of a Funerary Violinist, but by 1745, when Dominique Vernet wrote a letter to Graham Cockham deploring its use at the court of Louis XV (the earliest known reference to the practice), it was clearly already a contentious issue, and has remained so to this day. Vernet makes his own views plain:

> *These performing monkeys turn everything to a dance, in hope of gaining praise from their worldly masters, entirely unaware of the savage sacrilege they are committing with every single beat!!*

It is not known how Cockham felt on this matter, for his response is lost, but the views of a number of prominent Funerary Violinists have survived as it seems to have been a subject of considerable concern over the following hundred years, and was much written about.

When taken as a whole these various letters and other documents referring to the use of a drum demonstrate two clear and distinct views on the matter, in an argument that remains unchanged and valid to this day (the Guild of Funerary Violinists held a two-day debate on the subject in March 2003 – reaching the provisional conclusion that the 'judicious use of a drum', specifically a bass drum, was acceptable under certain clearly determined circumstances). On one side we have the aesthetic and spiritual purists who abhor the use of a drum, as they believe it undermines the necessary focus and intensity of the performance: amongst these are Siegfried Laudenslager, Charles Sudbury and Pierre Dubuisson. On the other side we have the pragmatists who believe that the 'judicious use of a drum' can add the necessary focus and intensity when the violinist himself is 'less exceptional'. These include Herr Gratchenfleiss, Archibald Elswick and Thomas Tullibody, amongst others. It is interesting that, of those who approve the use of a drum, there are no accounts surviving of their ever having been accompanied by a drum themselves; their support of the notion is always in the context of adding power to the performance of weaker Funerary Violinists, where the playing lacks the necessary nobility or substance.

The Guild of Funerary Violinists has itself changed its official attitude toward the use of a drum a number of times during its illustrious history. In 1772 Archibald Elswick, the then President of the Guild, commissioned a portrait from Gainsborough of himself performing at the graveside of his predecessor, Thomas Stotteridge, accompanied by the then Guild secretary, Jonas Cox, on a bass drum. Entitled *Funerary Music,* this portrait hung in the boardroom of the Guild's offices in Cavendish Square until 1829, when incoming President Charles Sudbury had it removed to the basement on the grounds that it seriously misrepresented the nature of the Art. Tragically, the painting was lost in the fire of 1841.

To get a flavour of the arguments for and against the use of a drum, let us consider the words of a few of the most important Funerary Violinists whose writings on the subject have survived.

In the Hildesheim Testament, Herr Gratchenfleiss offers a well-reasoned justification for its use in certain circumstances. Discovered in the Hildesheim trunk in 1983, the Testament includes a revealing paragraph on the subject:

There have been times, on my travels, that I have come upon poor village fiddlers attempting to do justice to the life of some recently deceased through the ludicrous misrepresentation of my own and others' works. Alas, where there should be strength and commitment there is nought but weakness and folly; where there should be focus and vigour there is nought but the vague blurring of a bow arm more suited to the use of a scythe; why even the mortal rhythms of our Art fall apart at their touch. That they have no talent is not their own fault, and they should not be condemned for that which is forcefully placed upon their shoulders. And it is indeed a common and deplorable sight all across Europe. However, on occasion I have come upon these self-same

*peasant fiddlers being accompanied in their funerary practices by the sol-
emn beating of a drum; and indeed the music is immediately transformed.
Although I was initially shocked by this intrusion upon our Art of the basest
of warlike instruments, once the horror of it had ceased to cloud my vision,
I was forced to deduce that, indeed, this was an answer to the problem; for
where there had been nought but weakness the drum offered strength; where
uncertainty had once prevailed the drum offered focus and commitment; and
the mortal rhythms of our Art held firm and solid as the ground. I have
therefore conceded over the years that, where the artistry of the Funerary
Violinist is less than exceptional, the judicious use of a drum can elevate the
performance to a level satisfactory for the appropriate funerary rites, and
therefore capable of the emotional and spiritual function therein …*

(Herr Hieronymous Gratchenfleiss, 1809)

Twenty years earlier, in 1789, Archibald Elswick, a great advocate of the use of a
drum, wrote a series of guidelines for the appropriate choice of instrument and
manner of performance, which was issued to all members of the Guild in October
of that year:

*If, having considered the various merits or otherwise of your playing you
decide to take up this course, then I offer the following strict recommenda-
tions which should be adhered to with absolute precision where possible:*

*The skin of the drum should be that of a male goat, seven years of age, and
in good health. The drum head should be no more than one and one half feet
in diameter, and the barrel no more than two feet deep. The sticks, no more
than one and one half feet long and made of birch or pine. These dimensions
should produce a tone of appropriate depth and punch without intruding too
greatly upon the substance of the music.*

*The drum should be played, where possible, by an apprentice Funerary
Violinist with no military experience. Military drummers are themselves
wholly inappropriate for the subtleties of the task, being used, as they are, to
beating out rhythms intended to inspire the greater will to win and overcome,
which would be both without taste and lacking of any meaning in the
funerary context. Circus drummers are still worse, and should at all times be
avoided. An apprentice Funerary Violinist should have the better understanding of the task that it is their duty to underline and not intrude upon. In*

addition, the experience should aid them in their own attempts toward mastery of the Art.

The drum should only be used to accompany the more strident and forthright elements of the funerary music, such as the procession and the interment itself. During those elements that symbolise reflection or release they should remain entirely silent. The drummer should always realise that his role is ritual, not musical, and should remain profoundly restrained throughout, satisfying himself with simple repetitive rhythms, and particularly those rhythms of mortal significance, such as the imitation of Death's knock at the door, which is in any case deeply woven into the music of the Funerary Violinist. They are beating the devils back into the ground, and should content themselves with nothing but the simple bold vigour necessary for such a task.

If these above rules are followed then the performance should be at the least satisfactory, although it should be mentioned that the pure simplicity of a solo Funerary Violinist, whose skill is equal to his intention, will always be the preferable option.

(Archibald Elswick, 1789) [translated from the original Latin]

In both of the above cases the use of a drum is being advocated in an attempt to improve the standard of funerary music performed by poor Funerary Violinists. However, Franz Kerchner, writing in 1810, went one step further, supporting the use of a suitable drum in all performances of Funerary Violin, for both its musical and its spiritual and symbolic implications. Kerchner, a friend of Herr Gratchenfleiss, and himself a practising Funerary Violinist in Mannheim, was also a keen amateur historian, with an interest in primitive cultures that was most unusual at the time. His elder brother, Ludwig Kerchner, who had inherited the family fortune, was an explorer and adventurer, who wrote one of the earliest accounts of Siberian shamanic religious practices, and kept Franz informed of all the latest accounts of primitive peoples published by the new breed of literary travellers. In a letter written to, but never received by, Herr Gratchenfleiss (who had died before it was sent), Kerchner states:

Among the writings and accounts of the many explorers and historians who have recently travelled the world in the noble quest for knowledge, there is frequent mention of pagan religious practices of the many primitive peoples encountered: and from these it can be seen that, since the dawn of Man, the solemn use of a drum has been the very key that opens the door to the many other worlds we have been so desirous of, over our long and varied history. Why, even the Egyptian Pharaohs had the images of drummers painted upon the walls of their tombs. Certainly the drum, like primitive Art, has not the sophistication of our modern civilised world, and it is a testament to our evolution beyond the primitive, that we take up the violin to lead our dead into the light — the violin; the most subtle and expressive instrument yet created: capable of lyricism, melody, harmony and rhythm; the only instru-ment that can become both a human voice and a fearsome beat in the very same breath ... But surely, to speak with all the eloquence of the civilised world to a door that remains closed is as meaningless as a Socratic conver-sation with a cat! Whether it be the door to the spirit-world, or the Gate of Heaven, is merely a matter of choice of words. The drum was our first great gift from God; the violin, a reward for the tremendous distance we have travelled. But in accepting the second we should not deny the first. For what is a palace without the humble ground on which it stands? Many of your own works are rooted on the strongest of mortal rhythms; rhythms dating back, in all likelihood, to our days as cave-dwellers; rhythms that formed the very foundations of our modern artistry, on which the unparalleled power of your own works are founded: so surely, to underline this eternal source of your own most wondrous of gifts can only serve to amplify their vision and cathartic glory ...

I have many times come upon the familiar sight of a village or small town funeral where your own works are boldly leading the procession, both to and from the church, to the accompaniment of a well judged bass drum. And, in all honesty, such music could not complement the mournful scene with greater depth or subtlety. Therefore I have, over the years, been forced to conclude that it is nothing short of a tragedy that many if not all of the better Funerary Violinists deem it to be a sign of weakness in their Art to make use of a drum in bolstering the profound implications of their work. If only a performer equal to your own great subtlety, ability, and spiritual presence were to embrace the undeniable pagan power of the drum to your own ends, I cannot even imagine the depth and scale of the journey they would be capable of taking us on, nor the implications for the cleansing of the Souls of the Dead that you so frequently mention in your own letters. Why, with such power in your hands you could cleanse the very army of the damned and send it, effervescent and sparkling, into the lap of Christ himself ...

If only a man of your unquestionable ability and fame were to demonstrate what I know to be not only possible, but to be demanded by the many legions of the Dead, who have, throughout time and history, been summoned by the beating of a drum, and embrace this path with all the charisma and authority of a worthy General, then I am sure the question of the drum would be resolved without any further argument, now and for all time. And, as such, the power of our most worthy of Arts would be so very amplified that the many dark spirits still wandering our mortal realm would at last be banished and sent to where they truly belong at the side of God. I therefore implore you to consider both my words and their meaning in the hope that you will engage with me in my vision of the future of our Art, as I know it to be both the will of Man and the will of God ...

(Franz Kerchner, 1810) [translated from the original German]

Tragically, Herr Gratchenfleiss died before this letter was sent (it was found amongst Kerchner's papers after his own death in 1831), but had he received it, it is unlikely he would have responded with anything other than disdain, despite his friendship with Kerchner and their obviously frequent correspondence, as referred to in the letter. Gratchenfleiss himself, along with all other known Funerary Violinists of great standing, had always taken the position that the pure voice of the solo violin, when in the hands of a great master, was the most potent of tributes both to the soul of the deceased and to God himself, and should not be sullied by any intrusion or accompaniment; and that any second voice could only serve to dilute the authentic power and commitment of the Art of Funerary Violin.

Of all the voices that stand against the use of a drum, in any circumstances, Charles Sudbury's is probably the most eloquent, and certainly the most melodramatic and condemnatory. In his *Considerations of the Funerary Arts* of 1838, he writes:

It is time to abandon once and for all this meaningless debate about the drum which has so preoccupied those of insufficient talent over the years. The point is very simple, if not elementary: would we employ an inadequate engineer to build a bridge? And then offer him an extra ton of iron to justify his lack of skill? Would we employ an inadequate surgeon to amputate a limb? And offer him an extra set of knives to aid in his insufficient ability? Would an additional palette of colours aid a talentless artist in rendering a likeness? Could a new edition of Dr Johnson's Dictionary elevate a simple rhymester to the heights of Shakespeare? In all cases I think not! And neither would the infantile pounding of a drum assist a Funerary Violinist who has not the talent nor skill to render his function adequately without it. The very notion is both monstrous and non-sensical. If a priest does not know the word of God, then he should not conduct Mass, with or without the help of incense and icons. Likewise if a Funerary Violinist cannot speak directly with the soul of the deceased through his playing, HE SHOULD NOT BE PLAYING! *The addition of a drum is nothing but a superfluous subterfuge set up as a decoy to the true issue at hand – that his lack of musicianship and mortal empathy makes him a poor if not foolish choice for the profound spiritual function asked of him.*

After much further castigation and vehemence, he goes on to describe why he believes the voice of a solo *unaccompanied* violin is so essential in demonstrating the art and purpose of the Funerary Violinist:

A Funerary Violinist is, by his very nature, a solitary soul, who bears upon his oft-furrowed brow a responsibility too great to be shared, too heavy to be weighed, and too fragile to be touched. It is his duty to stand at the very edge of the bold abyss, and to cast his net into the deep and the dark, like Peter, fishing for the souls of those in need of nourishment and cleansing, before their final voyage into God's own light. He is a musician, magician and priest; a conduit, catalyst and culmination: and in all these things he must stand alone, for only in his focused isolation can he truly speak as one to all about, as if whispering to them alone. His is the final conversation, touching and intimate, possessive and protective, a mother's embrace and a father's pride: and he alone can have the final word ... to trample upon this most poetic of intentions with the clumsy beating of a goat-skin would be an act of vandalism akin to sodomising the Pope!

Charmingly poetic as this explanation is, the same sentiments are put more clearly and directly by Pierre Dubuisson in a letter to Simone Blanchet, dated 17 September 1822:

It is the bold intimacy of a solo violinist that holds the key. The singing of a single voice has a power to transport and transform that is infinitely greater than the distant massed voices of choirs and orchestras. That solo violin, unpretentious, without pride or malice, can woo the spirit with an allure and intensity unimagined by those bold pretenders of pomp and ceremony. The solo violin encourages honesty, sincerity and trust; the drum, however, with its air of militarism, warlike and fierce, can only undermine the true purpose of the Funerary Violinist ... for in death, are we all not alone? In grief, are we all not alone? A crowd cannot speak to the lonely of heart. Only the single voice can reach those who are so very far from company, and with subtlety and compassion draw them back into the bosom of the world. [translated from the original French]

* * * * *

It is clear from this typical selection of documents that the use of a drum always was, and still is, a contentious issue, and that it is traditionally associated with inadequate ability on the part of the violinist himself. However, at the Guild's 2003 debate on the subject (as a part of the 2003 International Conference of Funerary Violinists held at the British Library in London, and hosted by the Guild of Funerary Violinists) it was concluded that, for the Art to survive and thrive in the modern world, a new set of criteria must be developed. Although the new guidelines are not due to be finalised until the ICFV of 2007, the initial conclusions were as follows:

It has been observed by those present, representing many organisations from many countries, whose aim is the promotion and exemplification of the Art of Funerary Violin, that our venerable practice today faces many new and uniquely modern challenges, and that the rising to these challenges demands the re-evaluation of a number of key issues, and the setting aside of certain traditions and customs that, though at one time to be greatly valued, may today be considered archaic and detrimental to the furtherance of our Art.

... It is essential for the continued evolution and practice of our Art, that a major drive of promotion and public demonstration be embarked upon, that Funerary Violin may, once again, be among the final thoughts of all who are by their nature mortal, and that all those involved in organising funerals and memorials, either by profession or family relation, be aware of the tremendous potency the employ of a Funerary Violinist can add to both the experience and memory of their event.

... It has been concluded that in today's world, where popular music is the dominant force in publicising, in all of the Arts, and where even Beethoven and Mozart seem only to be made digestible to the public through the addition of a popular beat, the judicious use of a drum in the execution of

Funerary Violin should be encouraged as a window through which our noble Art might be viewed by the public and attract the attention that it has been deprived of for so long. To this end we intend that the stigma for so long associated with the additional use of a drum be forever discarded and be replaced with a zest for the presentation of our Art in a manner that might embrace the modern world and bring our Funerary Violin once again to the centre of funerary activity.

After much discussion it has been concluded that the judicious use of a drum is entirely acceptable under the following circumstances:

1. *The drum should be performed in a restrained and ritualised manner, considering at all times its role as accompaniment, and never overly intruding into the substance of the piece being performed.*
2. *Its rhythms should be bold and repetitive, only ever exhibiting a subtle evolution throughout the duration of the individual piece.*
3. *The drum should only be used in those pieces that aspire toward the spirit of a march, be they in 3/4 or 4/4 time.*
4. *All programmes that include the use of a drum should in addition include a majority of works to be played unaccompanied, to ensure that the impression demonstrated of our Art is in keeping with its genuine spirit.*

(Minutes of the ICFV 2003 – The Guild of Funerary Violinists)

The Book of Scores

being a selection of the surviving scores

so far discovered

compiled by

Rohan Kriwaczek

The Guild of
Funerary Violinists

Contents of the
Book of Scores

Charles Sudbury –
Funerary Suite no.4 (1832)

The Erroneous Dirge of George Babcotte

George Babcotte
as recreated from a detailed written description,
by Thomas Dinsley, 1697

166

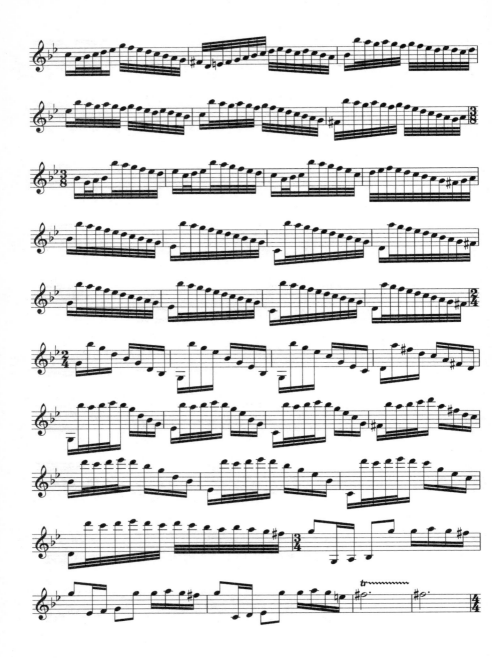

169

170

The Noble March of Death

Herr Hieronymous Gratchenfleiss

Slow, Heavy and Funereal - Bold and Declamatory

172

The Dizzy Flight of Death

Herr Hieronymous Gratchenfleiss

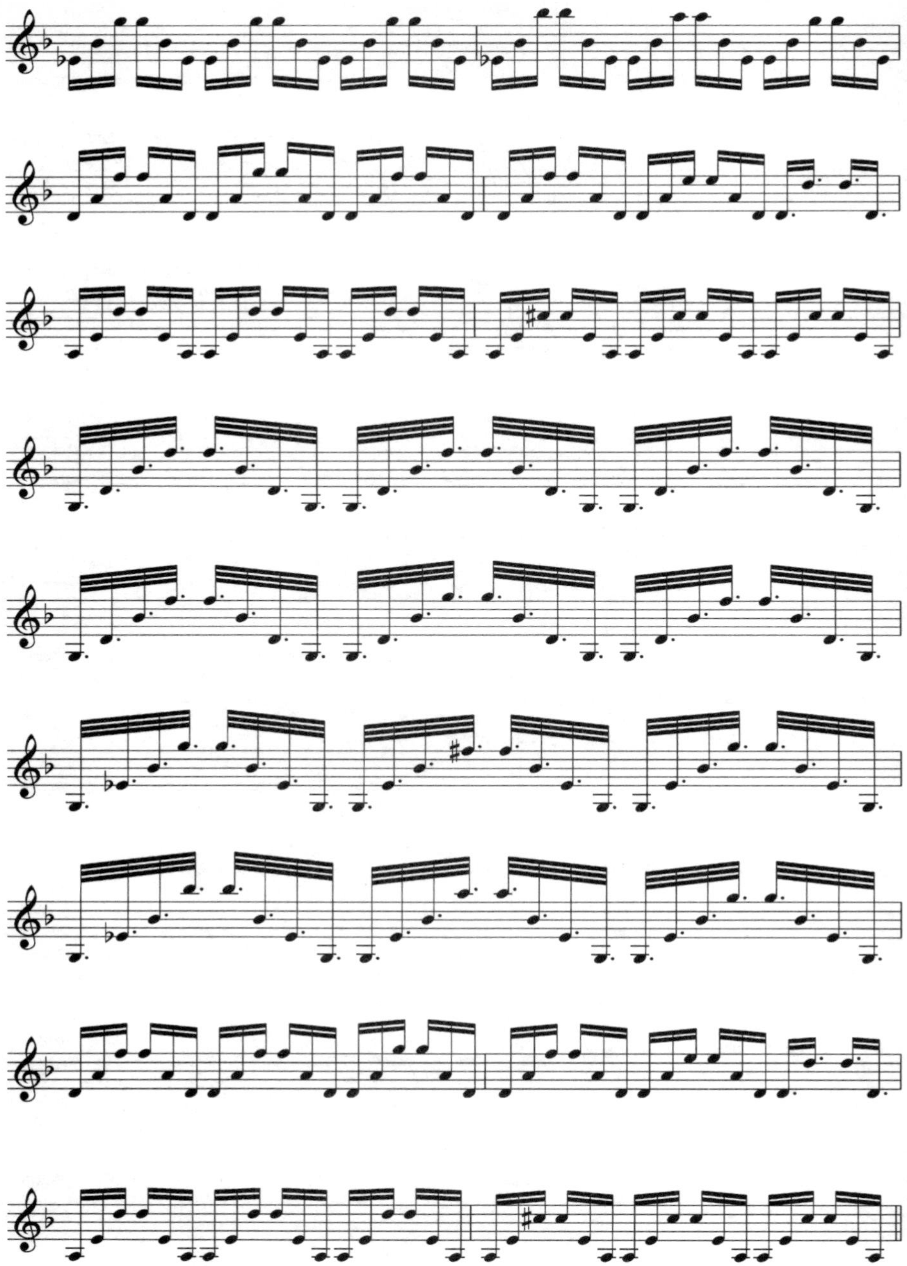

175

176

The Stately Tragedy of Death

Herr Hieronymous Gratchenfleiss

Not Too Slow - a Lyrical Dirge

178

The Masque of Death

Herr Hieronymous Gratchenfleiss

Slow, Stately and Refined

The Sultry Dance of Death

Herr Hieronymous Gratchenfleiss

A Steady Minuet, Dark and Doomladen

The Long Uncertainty of Death

Herr Hieronymous Gratchenfleiss

Light, Watery, Questioning, but Never Far from Melancholia

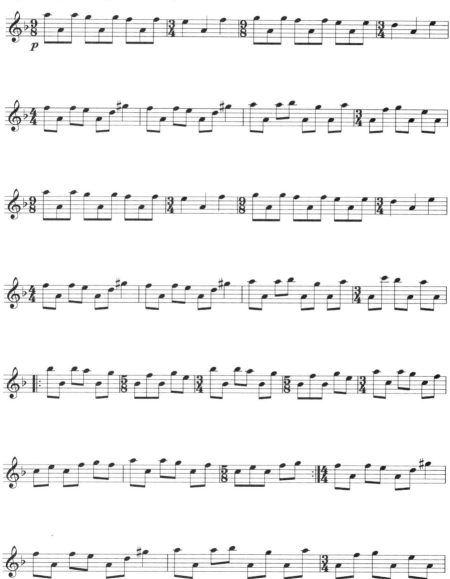

The Sombre Coquetry of Death

Herr Hieronymous Gratchenfleiss

Slow, Solid and Funereal

183

184

The Worthy Triumph of Death

Herr Hieronymous Gratchenfleiss

Slow, Heavy and Funereal, though not without the occasional Glimpe of Light.

185

Sept Regards sur l'Esprit de la Mort

Pour Monsieur E.M.

I. Marche Funèbre - Lent, posé et majestueux

Pierre Dubuisson 1826

II. Vol - Magnanime et degage

III. Marche Funèbre - *Sombre, pourtant ouvert sur l'avenir*

♩ = 70

Pierre Dubuisson 1826

189

IV. Éloge - Lyrique et couronné de tristesse

V. Panique - Panique momentanée - enraciné bien q'essayant de se sauver

Pierre Dubuisson 1826

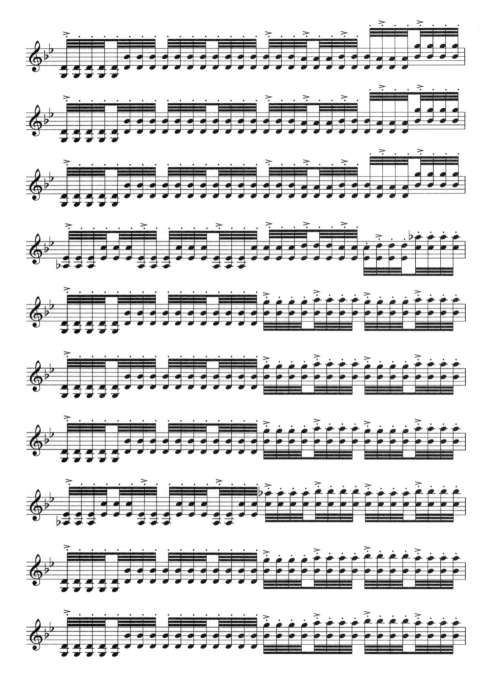

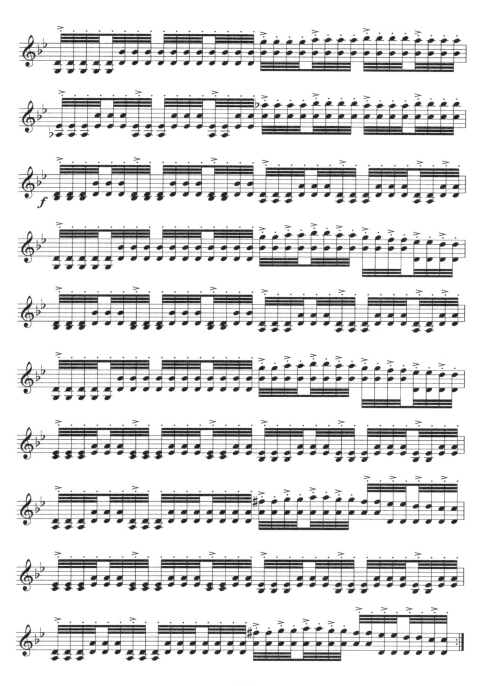

193

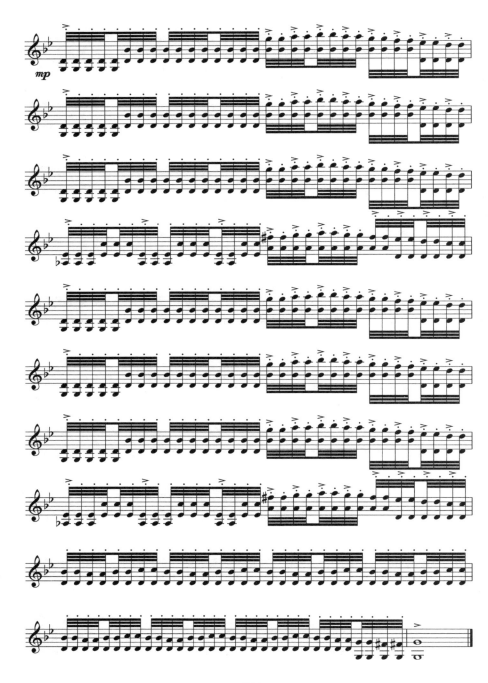

195

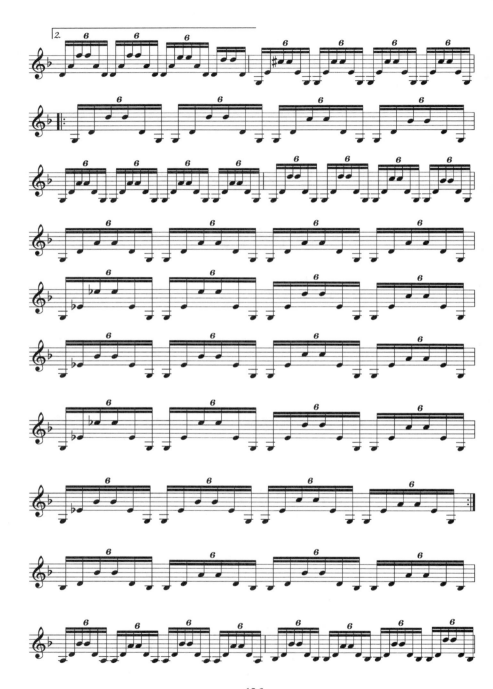

196

197

VII. Marche Funèbre - Triomphe de la tragédie

Pierre Dubuisson 1826

Funerary Suite no.4

*most humbly dedicated to the memory of Herr Hieronymous Gratchenfleiss
worthy leader of men, and undisputed master of his art*

Charles Sudbury 1832

I. March

*For the subtle approach of Death: to ease the fear
and calm the Soul's gentle mortification*

II. Introduction and March

To show the Soul's newfound delight,
and expel the sadness of those who mourn.

Charles Sudbury 1832

III. Dream

As the Soul looks down upon all that is laid aside,
a brief moment of grief before the bargaining begins.

Charles Sudbury 1832

IV. Panic

For the banishment of all spirits whose heart is not of purest white, and to
drive away the evil- minded ghosts that dwell where death is to be found.

Allegro con moto ♩=135

Charles Sudbury 1832

start **pp**, then increase volume with each repeat (**p**, **mp**, **mf**)

play 4 times

ff

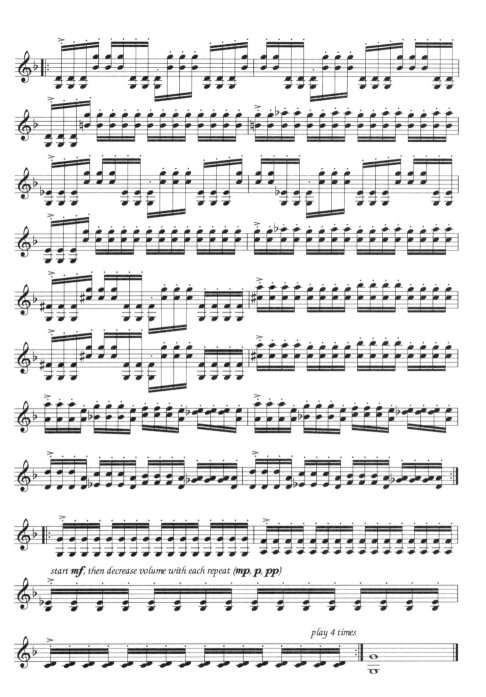

start *mf*, then decrease volume with each repeat (**mp**, **p**, **pp**)

play 4 times

205

V. Flight

*As if to dispel all doubts, the cleansed Spirit marks a final
path between God and Man, before its ultimate ascension.*

Charles Sudbury 1832

VI. Eulogy

*A final farewell as the Spirit rises unto God; not without sadness we
put our faith, and the spirit of our dead, in God's own hands.*

Charles Sudbury 1832

Adagio ♩ = 80

VII. March

Now that all is done and as it should be,
we may weep without reserve.

Da Capo